How To Know

THE EASTERN LAND SNAILS

Pictured-Keys for determining the Land Snails of the United States occurring east of the Rocky Mountain Divide

JOHN B. BURCH

Research Associate, Mollusk Division
Museum of Zoology, University of Michigan

WM. C. BROWN COMPANY PUBLISHERS
Dubuque, Iowa

Copyright © 1962
by
H. E. Jaques

Library of Congress Catalog Card Number 61-18612

THE PICTURED-KEY NATURE SERIES

"How to Know the Insects," Jaques, 1947

"Living Things—How to Know Them," Jaques, 1946

"How to Know the Trees," Jaques, 1946

"Plant Families—How to Know Them," Jaques, 1948

"How to Know the Economic Plants," Jaques, 1948, 1958

"How to Know the Spring Flowers," Cuthbert, 1943, 1949

"How to Know the Mosses and Liverworts," Conard, 1944, 1956

"How to Know the Land Birds," Jaques, 1947

"How to Know the Fall Flowers," Cuthbert, 1948

"How to Know the Immature Insects," Chu, 1949

"How to Know the Protozoa," Jahn, 1949

"How to Know the Mammals," Booth, 1949

"How to Know the Beetles," Jaques, 1951

"How to Know the Spiders," Kaston, 1952

"How to Know the Grasses," Pohl, 1953, 1968

"How to Know the Fresh-Water Algae," Prescott, 1954

"How to Know the Western Trees," Baerg, 1955

"How to Know the Seaweeds," Dawson, 1956

"How to Know the Freshwater Fishes," Eddy, 1957, 1969

"How to Know the Weeds," Jaques, 1959

"How to Know the Water Birds," Jaques-Ollivier, 1960

"How to Know the Butterflies," Ehrlich, 1961

"How to Know the Eastern Land Snails," Burch, 1962

"How to Know the Grasshoppers," Helfer, 1963

"How to Know the Cacti," Dawson, 1963

"How to Know the Aquatic Plants," Prescott, 1969

Other Subjects in Preparation

Printed in United States of America

INTRODUCTION

A general handbook of United States land shells has not appeared since Binney's 1885 *Manual of American Land Shells**, now out of print. Many of the land snail groups have since been revised and a number of changes, particularly in nomenclature, have been made. Most of these changes and revisions are recorded in Pilsbry's** monumental monographic treatment of the North American land snails, a work which has been indispensable in preparing the present handbook. Unfortunately, Pilsbry's monograph is often inaccessible to biology students.

The original intent of this contribution to the *Pictured-Key Nature Series* was to cover the entire United States land snail fauna. It was soon apparent, however, that this was too large a group to include under one cover, unless many species were left out. And because many species of land snails have a rather limited or localized distribution, and species common to one area often do not occur in other areas, it was felt that omission of many species, simply to conserve space, was undesirable.

The land snail species are nearly equally divided east and west of the Continental Divide, and each division contains for the most part a fundamentally different fauna. Therefore, a convenient and natural faunal division occurs at the eastern limit of the Rocky Mountains, and it is those snails found east of this divide that are included in this handbook.

The author is responsible for all illustrations, except those few made by Mr. Cushman, Staff Artist at the Museum of Zoology, University of Michigan. Mr. Cushman's drawings bear his initials, and appreciation is noted at this time for these illustrations.

Grateful acknowledgment is made to my colleague and former professor, Dr. Henry van der Schalie, Curator of Mollusks and Professor of Zoology, University of Michigan, for many kindnesses, including the use of the shell collections of the University's Museum of Zoology, for many suggestions concerning the manuscript, and for allowing me to use the several drawings prepared by Mr. Cushman. I am also indebted to Dr. Dorothea Franzen, Illinois Wesleyan University, for several helpful suggestions, to Mrs. Anne Gismann of our Museum for critically reading the manuscript, to Peggy Burch and

*United States National Museum Bulletin 28.

**Land Mollusca of North America (North of Mexico). The Academy of Natural Sciences of Philadelphia. Monographs, No. 3, Vols. 1 and 2. 1939-48.

Mary Heil for help in its preparation, and to Mr. Norman Reigle for help with many time-consuming chores.

Ann Arbor, Michigan

January 1, 1962

John B Burch

Snails are of high economic importance as well as having marked interest for the nature lover. Doctor Burch's manual is timely in making possible the ready identification of the Land Snails. His excellent drawings will be a valued aid in handling the keys and in making identifications.

Editor

CONTENTS

THE SNAILS (Mollusca: Gastropoda)

Snails* belong to the Phylum Mollusca, a large and very diverse group of animals of world-wide distribution. As mollusks they exhibit the diagnostic features which characterize the phylum; i.e., they are soft-bodied, unsegmented cóelomate animals. As gastropods they have a head, a ventral muscular foot, and a dorsal visceral hump which is usually enclosed in a hard calcarous shell (Fig. 1).

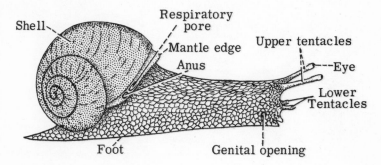

Figure 1. A typical land snail.

The shell of a typical land snail is generally a coiled tubular structure and functions to protect the animal from injury, predators, desiccation, and other unfavorable conditions of the environment. The lowest and usually largest coil is the body whorl, into which the animal can withdraw. The softest parts of the snail, containing most of the vital organs, always remain inside the shell. They are covered by a thin, tough skin called the mantle. The thickened part of the mantle bordering the aperture of the shell secretes calcium carbonate, thereby adding new shell around the aperture. By addition of new calcareous material in this manner, snails increase the size of their shells.

The outward shape of the typical snail is determined by its shell and flattened muscular foot. The shell is often of prime importance in species identification. The great diversity in structure, ornamentation, and color of snail shells has long made them a favorite of collectors.

The animal is covered dorsally by a tough, granular skin which is kept moist by numerous slime glands. The fleshy head joins directly to the foot and bears two pairs of tentacles and a pair of eyes. The mouth is at the anterior end and connects directly to a muscular pharynx containing a horny jaw and radula (Fig. 3). The pharynx is followed by a slender esophagus, a large, thin-walled crop, a smaller

---

*Slugs—snails without external shells—are usually included in the general usage of the term *snail* and are treated in this handbook.

stomach or gizzard, and a long coiled intestine which opens at the side of the animal near the respiratory pore (Fig. 2). The posterior tip of the body-foot is usually pointed and often contains a caudal pit.

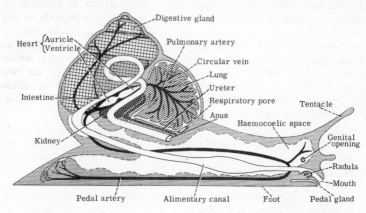

Figure 2. Internal anatomy of a land snail. The reproductive system is not shown.

A unique structure possessed only by mollusks is the radula, a ribbon-like organ with many fine chitinous teeth used in rasping food. When feeding, the radula is protruded through the mouth and moved across a cartilage by strong muscles. This allows the snail to rasp off particles of food over which it crawls. The great diversity in the form of the radular teeth among various groups of snails has been the basis for a large part of their classification.

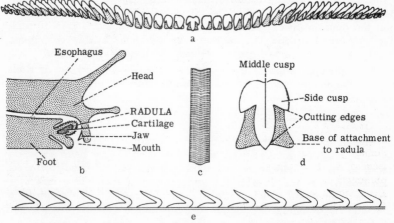

Figure 3. The radula. a, A transverse row of radular teeth; b, longitudinal section of a snail's head showing position of the radula; c, the entire radula showing the many transverse and longitudinal rows of teeth; d, central tooth enlarged; e, radular teeth in side view.

THE MOLLUSCA

The Phylum MOLLUSCA comprises a large group of animals of extremely divergent form that is second only to the arthopods in the number of described species (almost 100,000). Most mollusks have a hard external shell (although there are well-known exceptions such as the slugs and squids), a muscular sac-like covering (the mantle) which secretes the shell, soft bodies with no segmentation (except for two deep-sea species) or internal skeleton, numerous mucous or slime glands, and a large "foot" that is variously modified for crawling, digging, or grasping prey.

Mollusks are found in nearly all regions and habitats of the earth. They are found in deep-sea dredgings, in sandy, shallow lagoons, on coral reefs, in arctic waters, hot springs, in both tidal and freshwater mudflats, in swift mountain streams, deep lakes, temporary woods pools, in the ground, on the tops of high snow-covered mountains, in crater lakes, deserts, trees, densely populated urban areas, and even on and in other animals as parasites. They eat every possible food, e.g., soil micro-organisms, plankton, poisonous mushrooms, cactus plants, garden crops, refuse, paper, and fish. Some live on decayed land animals and their excrement. Others are known to be cannibals, eating their own species.

The shape of the foot has been used to recognize various assemblages of related species within the phylum as can be seen in the names given to the principal groups. There are six such groups, or classes, in the Mollusca (Fig. 4). Each class, except the chitons (Amphineura) and the two species of primitive mollusks (Monoplacophora), has a name which bears reference to the foot, i.e., Cephalopoda (head-foot), Gastropoda (stomach-foot), Scaphopoda (digging-foot), and Pelecypoda (axe-foot).

In addition to modifications of the locomotor organ, these groups are distinguished further by other features such as basic structure of

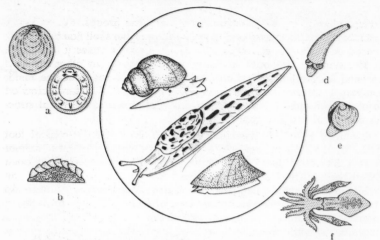

Figure 4. Representatives of the mollusk classes. a, *Neopilina*, dorsal and ventral views, MONOPLACOPHORA; b, chiton, side view, AMPHINEURA; c, snail, slug, and limpet, GASTROPODA; d, tusk shell, SCAPHO-PODA; e, clam, PELECYPODA; f, squid, CEPHALOPODA.

the shell, the absence, presence, or degree of development of the head, the degree of development of the nervous system and sense organs, modifications of the respiratory organs, and by the structure of the radula or teeth.

The Class MONOPLACOPHORA includes only two living species, both found in abyssal marine waters. The saucer-shaped, limpet-like shell covers a bilaterally symmetrical animal with a mouth in front and anus behind. The round ventral foot is surrounded by five pairs of gills. The paired pallial organs and gills suggest affinities with the annelid worms. The radular teeth and other characters demonstrate relationships with the chitons and other Amphineura.

The AMPHINEURA, another small primitive marine group, comprise the chitons (Polyplacophorans) and a series of deep-water, worm-like, shell-less forms (Aplacophorans). The shell of the chitons is divided into eight transverse calcareous plates (the only suggestion of segmentation) that cover the back. The foot is similar to that of the monoplacophorans (but more elongate) and also to that of the gastropods. The aplacophorans are covered by a mantle bearing minute calcareous spicules.

The GASTROPODA, the largest and most varied group of mollusks, include snails, slugs, sea-hares, and limpets. They are found in marine and fresh waters and on land. They have retained the primitive flat ventral foot adapted for crawling, but in other ways have evolved significantly from the ancestral type. They have all undergone a torsion in the general body plan so that the digestive tract is no longer a straight tube, but the anus comes to lie in the side of the animal, often near the head. Most gastropods have a coiled shell and,

4

correspondingly, a coiled visceral mass. In some groups, e.g., in many opisthobranchs (see below) and in the land slugs, the shell has become so reduced as not to appear externally at all. In some cases it is a small bit of calcareous material enclosed in the mantle; in other cases it has been lost entirely. This reduction of the shell has been the result of a long continued evolution; slugs are not snails that have crawled out of their shells. The shells of the limpets have lost the spiral structure and present a low conical shape.

The SCAPHOPODA are burrowing mollusks having a conical foot which, by alternating extensions and contractions, pulls the animal through the substratum. The mantle and shell are tubular and open at both ends. The shell is long and tapering and accounts for the common name of this group, the tusk shells. They are marine mollusks which do not carry on respiration by means of gills but by folds in the mantle lining.

The PELECYPODA, or Lamellibranchia, have an axe-shaped foot adapted for crawling or burrowing, and have completely lost the head and the buccal apparatus used by other mollusks in obtaining food. They are either marine, brackish, or fresh-water, and feed on microorganisms that are swept towards them by water currents created by fine hairs on the mantle and gills. The body is enclosed by two symmetrical mantle flaps which secrete right and left shell valves that are held together by a tough ligament. Because of this arrangement of the shell they are often referred to as "bivalves." This group includes the clams, oysters, and mussels, as well as the smallest pill-clams.

The CEPHALOPODA include the squids, octopuses, and nautiluses and are the most highly evolved of the mollusks. The foot has become divided into a number of prehensile "arms" or tentacles arranged symmetrically around the head or mouth, and from this close union of head and foot the class gets its name. A part of the foot is further modified to form a funnel which is used in swimming. By forcing water out of the mantle cavity through this funnel, the animal achieves water jet-propulsion. For short distances they are among the fastest creatures known. All cephalopods are marine and in many, such as the squid and octopus, the shell is internal or even lost.

THE GASTROPODS

The three subclasses of gastropods have been named in reference to the position or character of the respiratory apparatus. In the PROSOBRANCHIATA the breathing organ or gill is situated in front of the heart; in the OPISTHOBRANCHIATA it is behind the heart. The PULMONATA have replaced the gill by a vascular lung which may breathe either air or water depending on the habits of the particular species. Some prosobranchs and opisthobranchs have also lost their gills, but because of other details of their anatomy they are retained in their respective groups. The opisthobranchs are all marine, but both the prosobranchs and pulmonates have representatives in fresh and salt water, and on land. The pulmonates have very few marine or brackish-water species; the prosobranchs have relatively few land species.

In addition to respiratory and other anatomical differences, the pulmonates and prosobranchs usually can be distinguished by the presence or absence of an operculum or cover used to close the aperture when the snails are withdrawn into their shells (Fig. 5). Most prosobranchs have an operculum, but only the marine genus *Amphibola* of the pulmonates has such a protective structure.

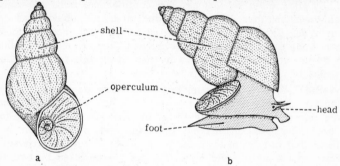

Figure 5. The prosobranch operculum. a, The operculum in the shell aperture, sealing off the interior of the shell; b, position of operculum while the snail is active.

The prosobranch snails included in this handbook represent two orders. The operculate land snails *Hendersonia, Lucidella* and *Helicina* belong to the primitive ARCHEOGASTROPODA and *Opisthosiphon, Chondropoma* and *Truncatella* to the large, extremely diverse, and widespread order MESOGASTROPODA.

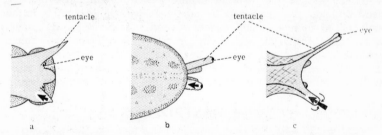

Figure 6. Position of the eyes and method of withdrawal of the tentacles in the three pulmonate snail orders. a, BASOMMATOPHORA, eyes at bases of a single pair of contractile tentacles; b, SYSTELLOMMA-TOPHORA, eyes at the tips of upper pair of contractile tentacles; c, STYLOMMATOPHORA, eyes at the tips of upper pair of retractile tentacles.

The pulmonate snails are divided into three large groups or orders —the Stylommatophora, the Systellommatophora, and the Basommatophora. The largest order is that of the land snails and slugs, the

STYLOMMATOPHORA, or Geophila. Characteristically the animals of this group have two pairs of tentacles, with eyes at the tips of the upper pair; the tentacles are retractile, i.e., can be inverted like a glove when the fingers are withdrawn (Fig. 6c). The SYSTELLOMMA-TOPHORA, or Gymnophila, comprise a small group of tropical slugs (e.g., *Veronicella*) also with eyes at the tips of the upper pair, but the tentacles are contractile (not inversible). The freshwater pulmonate snails have only one pair of tentacles, also contractile and the eyes are situated at their bases. These snails are placed in the Order BASOMMATOPHORA, or Limnophila.

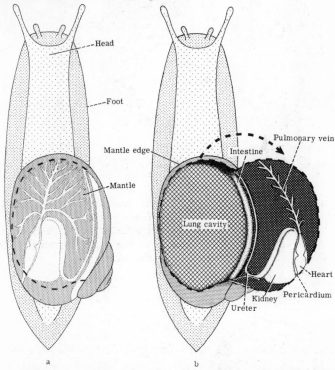

Figure 7. Pallial organs of a snail. a, Dorsal view of a snail with shell removed; the internal pallial organs are outlined; b, section of mantle cut along its edges and folded back to expose the pallial organs (heart, kidney, ureter, intestine).

The Stylommatophora are divided into four suborders, the Orthurethra, Mesurethra, Heterurethra, and Sigmurethra, on the basis of the internal structure and arrangement of the kidney and ureter (Figs. 7, 8). The SIGMURETHRA are the most advanced and by far the most important group in the United States with the greatest number of species. They differ from the others in that the ureter is abruptly reflexed from the apex of the kidney and passes to the posterior end of the lung cavity. It then follows the digestive tract anteriorly to the mantle edge. In the HETERURETHRA the ureter is not directed posteriorly, but only laterally to the intestine and then anteriorly to the pneumostomal opening. The ureter in the ORTHURETHRA does not run along the intestine, and in the MESURETHRA it is represented mainly by a lateral opening of the kidney.

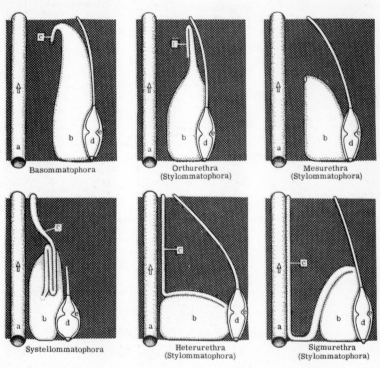

Figure 8. Form and arrangement of the kidney and ureter in pulmonate snails. Intestine (a), kidney (b), ureter (c), heart (d), pericardium (e). Arrow indicates direction of movement of material in the intestine.

The sigmurethran snails fall into two divisions according to the position of the pedal grooves of the foot. These two lateral grooves are found at the boundaries where the tuberculate side walls of the foot join the smooth ventral sole. In the HOLOPODA, such as *Haplotrema*, *Lamellaxis*, *Holospira*, *Bulimulus*, *Thysanophora*, *Polygyra*, *Cepolis*, *Helicella* and *Helix*, the pedal grooves are inconspicuous and in or close to the angle of the lateral margins of the foot. In the AULACOPODA, e.g., *Philomycus*, *Arion*, *Anguispira*, *Deroceras*, *Oxychilus*, *Zonitoides*, *Retinella*, *Euconulus* and *Testacella*, they are situated higher so that part of the sole actually comes around to form part of the vertical side of the foot. Among snails or slugs of this latter group there is a second rather weakly impressed groove above and running parallel to the pedal groove, the suprapedal groove (see Fig. 15).

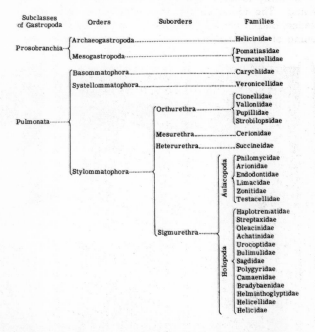

Fig. 9. Higher classification of the eastern land snails (modified from Pilsbry).

MOLLUSCAN PROVINCES IN THE UNITED STATES

The land snail faunas of the eastern and western United States are fundamentally different. In addition, the fauna of the southern tips of Texas and Florida is quite different from that of the rest of North America. This southern fauna is really part of a much larger Middle American fauna, which also inhabits the West Indies, Bermuda, Central America and most of Mexico. Thus, in respect to its land snail faunas, the United States, may be divided into three major divisions: East, West and Middle American. And since the physical barriers separating these regions are not impassable, their boundaries are not distinct lines, but rather broad transitional zones.

The Eastern and Western Divisions are each subdivided into several molluscan provinces, less distinctly and sharply defined than the Divisions, but nevertheless each having its own more or less distinctive land snail fauna. The Eastern Division, of main concern here, extends

from the plains bordering the eastern limit of the Rocky Mountains to the Atlantic Coast. It consists of the Northern, Interior, Cumberland, Texan and Austroriparian provinces. The approximate limits of these regions are shown in Figure 10.

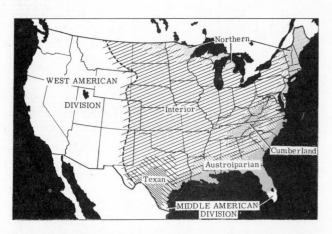

Figure 10. Molluscan provinces in the East American Division (shaded) and its relation to the other Divisions in the United States.

The following species occur in both the Eastern and Western divisions (those marked with an asterisk also occur naturally on other continents; those marked with a double asterisk are foreign introduced species; those with three asterisks are native North American species introduced on other continents).

10

Cionella lubrica*

Vallonia pulchella*
Vallonia gracilicosta
Vallonia perspectiva
Vallonia cyclophorella

Columella edentula*
Columella alticola
Vertigo ovata
Vertigo gouldi
Vertigo modesta
Pupilla blandi
Pupilla muscorum*
Gastrocopta pentodon
Gastrocopta tappaniana
Gastrocopta procera
Gastrocopta cristata
Gastrocopta pellucida hordeacella

Succinea grosvenori
Succinea luteola

Arion ater**
Arion hortensis**
Arion fasciatus**
Arion intermedius**

Punctum minutissimum
Punctum californicum
Helicodiscus eigenmanni
Helicodiscus singleyanus

Discus cronkhitei
Anguispira kochi

Milax gagates**
Deroceras reticulatum**
Deroceras laeve**
Lehmannia poirieri**
Limax maximus**
Limax flavus**

Striatura meridionalis
Zonitoides nitidus*
Zonitoides arboreus***
Hawaiia minuscula***
Retinella electrina
Retinella binneyana
Retinella indentata
Oxychilus cellarius**
Oxychilus draparnaldi**
Oxychilus alliarius**

Holospira roemeri

Bulimulus dealbatus
Bulimulus schiedeanus

Thysanophora horni

Cochlicella ventrosa**

Helix aspersa**
Cepaea nemoralis(?) **

In addition to those genera with species listed above, Carychium, Catinella, Oxyloma, Euconulus, Haplotrema, Allogona and Triodopsis also occur in both Eastern and Western divisions. On the other hand, many important genera are found in one division but not in the other. In the Eastern Division the following are characteristic (although those marked with an asterisk extend also into Middle America):

Hendersonia
Strobilops*
Pallifera*
Philomycus
Ventridens
Clappiella
Gastrodonta
Pilsbryna

Paravitrea
Vitrinizonites
Mesomphix*
Mesodon
Praticolella*
Stenotrema
Polygyra*

The most distinct molluscan province in the Eastern Division is the Cumberland, which has several special genera (*Clappiella*, *Gastrodonta*, *Pilsbryna* and *Vitrinizonites*) and many endemic species. The Austroriparian Province, covering the southern and the southeastern coastal plain, and the Texan Province are characterized by the prevalence of *Polygyra*. In the latter province there is found a predominance of *Polygyra texasiana* and related species, while in the Austroriparian Province there is a prevalence of *Polygyra* of the *septemvolva* and *auriculata* types. The Northern Province does not differ greatly in the characteristics of its land snail fauna from that of the Interior Province, but its climate is too severe for any but the most hardy species. Its species are mainly small zonitids and pupillids.

The known distribution in both the eastern and western U.S.A. is given for each species with the pictured-key for the eastern species.

HABITS OF LAND SNAILS AND SLUGS

Native land snails and slugs may be found almost everywhere, but in general prefer habitats offering shelter, adequate moisture, and abundant food supply, and for snails, generally an available source of lime. Forested river valleys most generally supply such habitats, and those with outcrops of limestone usually show the most abundant and varied mollusk faunas. Introduced species often tend to be somewhat more urban. For example, in its native Europe the slug *Milax gagates* lives in woodlands and on damp rocks on open hillsides and is not a slug of cultivated areas. But in the United States it is mostly found around dwellings and in greenhouses and gardens.

Land snails and slugs are mainly nocturnal, but following a rain they may come out of their hiding places during the day. Temperature and moisture are the main factors to account for their nocturnal habits, and not the presence of darkness per se. During the day they may be found resting under old boards and logs, under bricks and stones, in rock piles and cellars, among hedge rows, and beneath damp refuse and litter. Snails are more adaptable to unfavorable environmental conditions, such as drought, because they can cover the aperture of their shells with an operculum or a mucous sheet, the epiphragm, which hardens and thereby prevents desiccation. Some snails have been known to remain in this dormant state for years, only to come out and resume activity when they are moistened.

Most land snails and slugs pass the winter in sheltered places under stones, logs, and boards, or buried in the ground. Some snails are not so secretive, surviving in the open on such objects as tree trunks and fence posts during periods of unfavorable humidity and temperature.

IDENTIFICATION

Since the main purpose of this handbook is the identification of snails and slugs, it will be necessary to go into some detail on characters to be looked for and used in making species determinations. Many of these characters are illustrated in Figures 11-15. Necessary equipment for identification will usually include at the most a 10X hand lens.

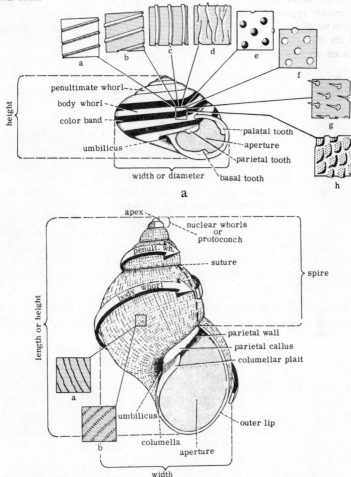

Figure 11. Shell terminology and surface sculpture. 11a, Striae (indented spiral lines) (a), lirae (raised spiral lines) (b); ribs (raised transverse lines) (c); wrinkles (d); puncta or pits (e); papillae or granules (f); hairs or bristles (g); dents (malleated) (h). 11b, Transverse or growth lines (a); spiral lines or striae (b).

The size and general form of the shell are important in recognizing snails. Its shape may take many forms, from very elongate (Fig. 12, a) to globose (Fig. 12, e, m), depressed (Fig. 12, n, o), and discoidal (Fig. 12, p). It may be either higher than wide, or wider than high. Its coils may turn either to the left or right (Fig. 12, u, v), be round (Fig. 12, i, t), angular (Fig. 12, s), shouldered (Fig. 12, g, h) or flattened (Fig. 12, f), and have shallow, impressed, or crenulated sutures (Fig. 12, b, c, d).

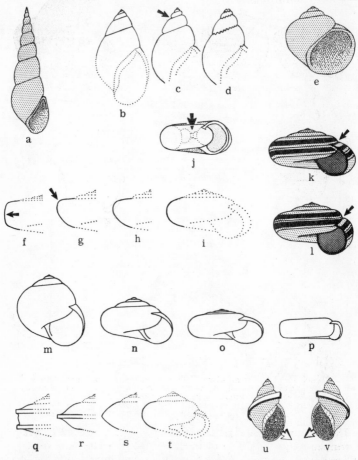

Figure 12. Shell terminology. a, Shell with whorls increasing gradually in size; b, sutures slightly indented; c, sutures strongly indented; d, crenulate sutures; e, whorls rapidly increasing in size; f, flattened whorl; g, shouldered whorl; h, moderately shouldered whorl; i, rounded whorl; j, sunken spire; k, last whorl not descending in front, i.e., not deflected; l, last whorl descending in front, i.e., deflected; m, globose shell; n, depressed shell; o, strongly depressed shell; p, discoidal shell; q, doubly carinate periphery; r, carinate periphery; s, angular periphery; t, round periphery; u, dextrally (to the right) whorled shell; v, sinistrally (to the left) whorled shell.

The shell may have few or many whorls (Fig. 13, e illustrates how they are counted), may lack an opening (umbilicus) in its base, or may have either a narrow or wide one (Fig. 13, a, b, c). Its columella, or central axial column, may be twisted or straight, and may or may not end abruptly (Fig. 13, i, j). Its outer lip may be straight or variously curved (Fig. 13, f, g, h), and is sometimes turned back, or reflected (Fig. 13, l).

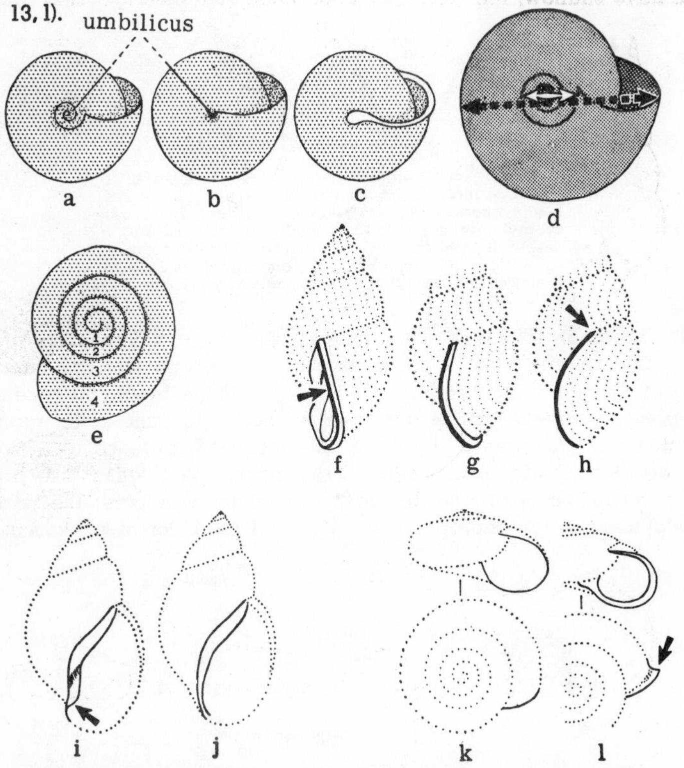

Figure 13. Shell terminology. a, Umbilicate shell; b, perforate shell; c, imperforate shell; d, method of measuring shell and umbilicus diameters; e, method of counting whorls; f, straight outer lip; g, curved outer lip; h, lip retracted to the suture; i, truncate columella; j, straight columella; k, straight (not reflected) lip; l, reflected lip.

The surface of the shell may be marked, i.e., colored or sculptured, in various ways (Fig. 11), or may be simply white and smooth. The outline of the aperture, due to the shape and relation of the whorls to each other and to calcareous deposits, may take many forms, the more common ones shown in Fig. 14, a-i. The aperture may or may not be closed by an operculum (Fig. 5) which itself has important characters. The operculum may be round, oval or spindle-shaped, and concentric, paucispiral, or multispiral, depending on the way in which it is formed (Fig. 14, j-m). It may also be subspiral (see Figs. 21 and 63).

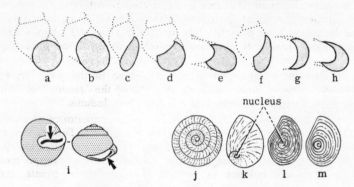

Figure 14. Shell terminology. a, Round aperture; b, oval aperture; c, narrowly oval aperture; d, roundly lunate aperture; e, ovate-lunate aperture; f, narrowly ovate-lunate aperture; g, broadly lunate aperture; h, deeply lunate aperture; i, narrow slit-like aperture; j, multispiral operculum; k, paucispiral operculum; l, concentric operculum; m, concentric operculum with spiral nucleus.

In the slugs (Fig. 15), the general size, shape and contour of the body, and relative size of the mantle are important. Other characters used in their identification are: the position of the breathing pore, and the presence or absence of a groove in the mantle; the color, pigment patterns, and texture of the skin; the presence, absence, or relative size of a sharp ridge, or keel, on the back; the relative size of the neck; the presence or absence of a caudal mucous pore; the relative development of the suprapedal groove; and the color of the mucus.

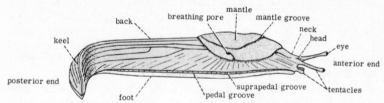

Figure 15. Slug terminology.

ECONOMIC IMPORTANCE

The economic importance of snails and slugs to man may be considered from two different aspects—that of a "positive" or beneficial nature and that of a "negative" or harmful nature. Under the positive aspects our native snails are probably of most importance to man in an indirect way as part of natural food chains. In the economy of nature their role is a valuable one in that they help maintain the balance of life as it is found in natural communities. Snails serve as food for such animals as frogs, salamanders, newts, turtles, mice, moles, shrews, squirrels, and birds.

16

The Edible Snail (*Helix pomatia*) is sufficiently important as human food in some European countries to make its cultivation a regular industry. However, none of the native Eastern United States land snails are as large as *Helix pomatia*, and none are eaten by people now, although some species in the past served as food for the American Indian.

In addition to being eaten, snails have also in the past figured importantly in trade. Snail shells have provided the "money" of various races, including the "wampum" of American Indians.

From the negative point of view the economic importance of snails and slugs comes under three general categories: (1) Destruction of crops and gardens; (2) medical importance, both to man and his domestic animals; and (3) indirect effects resulting from immigrant mollusks affecting the balance of natural communities of plants and animals.

Destruction of Crops and Gardens

The land snails and slugs are of most concern as agricultural pests, while the fresh-water snails are of greater importance from the medical standpoint. Approximately 725 species of land snails and about 40 species of slugs are now recognized in the United States (exclusive of Alaska and Hawaii). Of these species 54 (44 snails and 10 slugs) are not native to the country, but they have been introduced either accidentally or purposely.

With the exception of a few cases, *the native species are solitary in habit and do very little or no damage*. The introduced snails and slugs are usually the most undesirable, because they are gregarious or colonial and may cause great damage by building up enormous populations over limited areas. They are of considerable economic importance through their depredations in greenhouses, gardens, and orchards. In many places they have caused as much damage to vegetables, ornamentals, and other plants as certain insect pests. Snails and slugs through their presence on walks, around foundations and in cellars are also annoying to householders. Eradication of these pests is difficult and often costly.

Among the more serious foreign garden pests already established in this country are the slugs *Limax maximus*, *L. flavus*, and *Deroceras reticulatum*. Commercial interchange of plants, cuttings, and floricultural materials facilitates their dispersal. The snails *Helix aspersa* and *Otala lactea* have become established in California and considerable expense, time, and energy have been devoted to combating them. *Theba pisana*, an especial nuisance to citrus crops and at one time also well established in that State, apparently has been completely eradicated now.

One of the most serious threats to this country in recent years has come from the giant African snail *Achatina fulica*. This voracious eater with an enormous reproductive capacity began its immigration from East Africa via human agencies about the turn of the 19th century. In the intervening years this snail has spread to India, Ceylon, the mainland of China, and the East Indies. Its dispersal in the Pacific Islands, nearly denuding some of them, was greatly facilitated during World War II by the rapid conquest of this area by the Japanese. They introduced the snail as a supplemental food source to many new places including New Guinea, New Britain, and New Ireland. The snail was introduced into Hawaii in 1936 and has subsequently cost the taxpayers some $200,000 for control measures, not counting the damage to plants in that area. In 1948 it was brought to California on equipment returned from war areas, but an intensive campaign prevented its establishment. Nevertheless, constant vigil must be maintained to insure that it is not introduced again and does not become established.

Medical Importance to Man and His Domestic Animals

Snails, as required intermediate hosts in the life cycle of parasitic trematode worms infecting man and his domestic animals, occupy a position of utmost importance in man's war against disease. Their role in sustaining the parasitic worm larvae indirectly implicates them as responsible for some of the most serious and economically important human communicable infections. These diseases, however, are usually associated with tropical regions, and are either absent or of little import in the United States.

Although nearly every kind of mollusk is inhabited by some form of worm parasite, only relatively few snails are of medical or veterinary importance. Of these, almost all live in fresh water. A few land snails, e.g., *Cionella lubrica*, are vectors of lancet liver flukes in domestic and wild mammals (sheep, cattle, deer, and woodchucks); other land snails (*Zonitoides arboreus* and *Anguispira alternata*) are implicated in the spread of lungworms in domestic sheep in the U.S.A.

Effects on Natural Communities of Plants and Animals

It may seem that introduced foreign snails and slugs would be of little concern to man if they could be kept out of gardens, orchards, and greenhouses, and were not capable of carrying disease organisms. However, such an assumption is likely to be erroneous because the undesirable effects of snails in uncultivated areas may not become apparent immediately or even for a considerable time.

Natural communities, if not disturbed too greatly by outside influences, become stabilized structural entities, consisting of all the plants and animals which normally constitute the community coexisting in a more or less mutually satisfactory association. These animals and plants stand in a special relation to one another, the community organization depending chiefly on the manner in which they are interrelated, both among themselves and with their physical and chemical environment. Plants not only provide shelter and protection for other plants and animals, but supply food for the vegetarians or herbivores, which in turn tend to keep the plants from becoming too abundant. The number of plant feeders in the community is to a large extent controlled by carnivores and parasites.

The introduction of an animal, such as a strange snail, whose habits and fecundity are completely foreign to the community while its parasites or predators are usually absent, may have rather profound and adverse effects on the organization of the community and nearly every organism in it. The immigrant snails, in building up a large population, may not only out-compete the native well-regulated snails and other herbivores for food, but also by destroying vegetation deprive many organisms of essential shelter. Reduction in abundance or disappearance of the native herbivores results in the reduction or extinction of many carnivorous species, which may then affect other members of the community, either by removing a check in their increase or depriving them of a livelihood. This unbalanced state may cause many beneficial animals and plants to disappear permanently from the area. Therefore, the indirect economic importance of an introduced species may actually be far greater than the direct and more obvious economic impact.

SELECTED REFERENCES

American Malacological Union. 1955. *How to collect shells* (a symposium). Buffalo. Pp. 75.

Archer, Allan F. 1948. Land snails of the Genus *Stenotrema* in the Alabama region. *Geological Survey of Alabama, Museum Paper 28.* Pp. 85.

Baker, Frank Collins. 1902. *The Mollusca of the Chicago area.* Part II. Natural History Survey of the Chicago Academy of Sciences. Bulletin *3*(2): 137-410.

—————. 1939. *Fieldbook of Illinois land snails.* State of Illinois Natural History Survey Division, Manual 2. Pp. 166.

Baker, H. Burrington. 1909. Key to the genera of Gastropoda of Michigan. *Eleventh Report of the Michigan Academy of Science.* Pp. 134-140.

—————. 1930. The North American Retinellidae. *Proceedings of the Academy of Natural Sciences of Philadelphia, 82:* 193-219.

Bartsch, Paul. 1931. *Mollusks.* Smithsonian Scientific Series, *10*(3): 251-357.

Binney, William G. 1885. *Manual of American land shells.* United States National Museum Bulletin *28.* Pp. 526.

Binney, W. G. and T. Bland. 1869. *Land and fresh water shells of North America.* Part I. Pulmonata Geophila. Smithsonian Miscellaneous Collections, 194. Pp. 316.

Brooks, Stanley T. 1931. A list of the land snails of Pennsylvania with a summary of their distribution. *Carnegie Museum Annals, 22*(3-4): 313-331.

Burch, John B. 1960. *Some snails and slugs of quarantine significance to the United States.* Agricultural Research Service, United States Department of Agriculture, *82*(1). Pp. 73.

Burch, Paul R. 1950. Mollusks. *In: The James River Basin. Past, Present and Future.* Virginia Academy of Science. Pp. 129-137.

Call, R. Ellsworth. 1900. A descriptive illustrated catalogue of the Mollusca of Indiana. *24th Annual Report of the Department of Geology and Natural Resources of Indiana.* Pp. 335-535.

DeKay, James E. 1843. *Natural history of New York.* Part V. Mollusca. Carroll and Cook, Albany. Pp. 271.

Goodrich, Calvin. 1932. *The Mollusca of Michigan.* University Museums, University of Michigan, Michigan Handbook Series, No. *5.* Pp. 120.

Goodrich, Calvin, and Henry van der Schalie. 1944. A revision of the Mollusca of Indiana. *The Amercian Midland Naturalist. 32*(2): 257-326.

Hubricht, Leslie. 1953. Land Snails of the Southern Atlantic Coastal Plain. *The Nautilus, 66*(4): 114-125.

Jacobson, Morris K. 1959. The land snails around us. Parts 1 and 2 *Audubon Magazine, 61* (2 and 3): 68-71, 124-125.

Karlin, Edward J. and John A. Naegele. 1960. Biology of the Mollusca of Greenhouses in New York State. *Agricultural Experiment Station, Cornell University, Memoir 372.* Pp. 35.

Leonard, A. Byron. 1959. *Handbook of gastropods in Kansas.* Museum of Natural History, University of Kansas. Miscellaneous Publication No. *20.* Pp. 224.

Letson, Elizabeth J. 1905. Check list of the Mollusca of New York. *New York State Education Department, Bull. 341.* Pp. 112.

MacMillan, Gordon K. 1949. The land snails of West Virginia. *Annals of the Carnegie Museum, 31*(7): 89-207.

Mazÿck, William Gaillard. 1913. Catalog of Mollusca of South Carolina. Contributions from the Charleston Museum, *2.* Pp. 39.

Morse, Edward S. 1864. Observations on the terrestrial Pulmonifera of Maine, including a catalogue of all the species of terrestrial and fluviate Mollusca known to inhabit the State. *Journal of the Portland Society of Natural History.* 1(1): 1-63.

Morton, J. E. 1958. *Molluscs.* Hutchinson University Library, London. Pp. 232.

Pilsbry, H. A. 1897-1898. A classified catalogue with localities of the land shells of America north of Mexico. *The Nautilus, 11*(4-12): 45-48, 59-60, 71-72, 83-84, 93-96, 105-108, 117-120, 127-132, 138-144.

——————. 1900. Mollusca of the Great Smoky Mountains. *Proceedings of the Academy of Natural Sciences of Philadelphia.* Pp. 110-150.

——————. 1903. Mollusca of Western Arkansas and adjacent States, with a revision of *Paravitrea. Proceedings of the Academy of Natural Sciences of Philadelphia.* Pp. 193-214.

——————. 1939-1948. *Land Mollusca of North America (North of Mexico).* The Academy of Natural Sciences of Philadelphia. Monographs, No. *3,* Vols. 1 and 2. Pp. 2215.

Robertson, Imogene C. S. and Clifford L. Blakeslee. 1948. *The Mollusca of the Niagara Frontier Region.* Bulletin of the Buffalo Society of Natural Sciences, *19*(3): 1-191.

Sterki, V. 1896. Analytical keys for identifying the land Mollusca of Ohio. *Fifth Annual Report of the Ohio State Academy of Science.* Pp. 18.

——————. 1907. A preliminary catalogue of the land and freshwater molluscs of Ohio. *Proceedings of the Ohio State Academy of Science,* 4(8): 367-402 (Special Paper 12).

Taylor, John W. 1894-1900. Monograph of the land and freshwater Mollusca of the British Isles. Vols. I, II, III. Taylor Brothers, Publishers, Leeds. Pp. 1288.

Turner, H. W. 1883. Mollusca. *In: South Carolina: Resources and Population, Institutions and Industries.* South Carolina—State Board of Agriculture. Walker, Evans and Cogswell. Charleston. Pp. 298-304.

Walker, Bryant. 1900. The origin and distribution of the land and freshwater Mollusca of North America. *First Report of the Michigan Academy of Science.* Pp. 43-61.

—————. 1906. An illustrated catalogue of the Mollusca of Michigan. Part I. Terrestrial Pulmonata. Report for 1905. *Michigan State Board of Geological Survey.* Pp. 437-507.

—————. 1928. *The terrestrial shell-bearing Mollusca of Alabama.* Museum of Zoology, University of Michigan, Miscellaneous Publications, No. *18.* Pp. 180.

Walker, Bryant, and Henry A. Pilsbry. 1902. The Mollusca of the Mt. Mitchell Region, North Carolina. *Proceedings of the Academy of Natural Sciences of Philadelphia.* Pp. 413-442.

Winslow, Mina L. 1921. Mollusca of North Dakota. *Museum of Zoology, University of Michigan, Occasional Paper 98.* Pp. 18.

—————. 1926. A revised check list of Michigan Mollusca. *Museum of Zoology, University of Michigan, Occasional Paper 181.* Pp. 28.

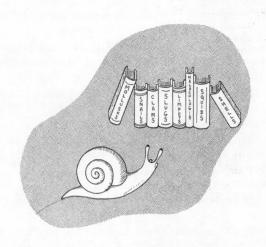

PICTURED-KEY TO EASTERN U. S. LAND SNAIL FAMILIES*

1a Aperture of shell closed by an operculum (Fig. 16). Sub-class *Prosobranchia*.......2

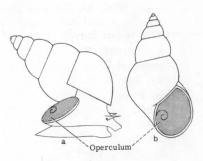

Figure 16

1b Aperture of shell not closed by an operculum, or shell entirely absent (Fig. 17b). Subclass *Pulmonata*.......4

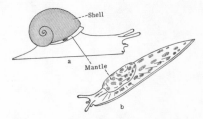

Figure 17

**2a Shell wider than high, without ribs; sutures not impressed (Fig. 18). Order *Archaeogastropoda* ....
....Family HELICINIDAE, page 36**

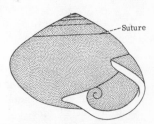

Figure 18

*The keys in this handbook are based on adult characters, usually those of the shell. A key which would also include immature shell characters would either be almost impossible to construct, or too cumbersome to use.

Cessation of growth in many species is accompanied by a thickening or reflection of the aperture lip of the shell. Sometimes one or more calcareous projections or "teeth" are deposited in the aperture. Adults in those species are easily distinguished from immature individuals. In other species, however, it is more difficult to determine when a shell belongs to an adult. Of particular use in distinguishing adults in such cases is the relation of the number of whorls of the shell to its size. Therefore, adult shell sizes and whorl counts are given for all species with external shells.

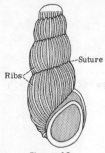

Suture

Ribs

Figure 19

2b Shell higher than wide, usually sculptured with either fine or coarse ribs; sutures moderately to rather strongly impressed (Fig. 19). *Order Mesogastropoda* 3

Figure 20

3a Shell relatively large (8 mm. or more in length), dull, sculptured with many fine ribs, umbilicate (see Fig. 13, a); operculum spiral (Fig. 20)...Family POMATIASIDAE, page 38

Figure 21

3b Shell relatively small (less than 8 mm. in length), polished, imperforate (see Fig. 13, c); ribs, when present, thick; operculum subspiral (Fig. 21).... ....Family TRUNCATELLIDAE, page 39

4a Head with one pair of tentacles, eyes at bases of tentacles (see Fig. 6, a); animal and shell minute; shell elongate (but not pupa-shaped), lip reflected (see Fig. 13, 1), aperture usually with one tooth or lamella. *Order Basommatophora*...Family CARYCHIIDAE, page 41

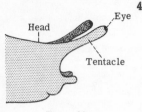

Head

Eye

Tentacle

Figure 22

4b Head with two pairs of tentacles, eyes at the tips of the upper pair of tentacles (Fig. 22); animal and shell (when present) minute to large; shell, when present, elongate (Figs. 25, c-i), globose or depressed (Fig. 12, m, n, o) (when elongate and having a reflected lip it either lacks apertural teeth, or has more than one) 5

5a Tentacles contractile (Fig. 23); animal without a shell.
Order *Systellommatophora*.........................
................Family VERONICELLIDAE, page 42

Figure 23

5b Tentacles retractile (Fig. 24); animal with or
without a shell. *Order Stylommatophora*......6

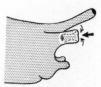

Figure 24

6a Shell pupa-shaped (Fig. 25, c), 20 mm. or more in length. *Suborder
Mesurethra*........................Family CERIONIDAE, page 67

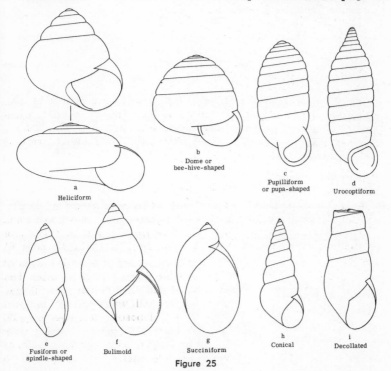

a
Heliciform

b
Dome or
bee-hive-shaped

c
Pupilliform
or pupa-shaped

d
Urocoptiform

e
Fusiform or
spindle-shaped

f
Bulimoid

g
Succiniform

h
Conical

i
Decollated

Figure 25

6b Shell, when present, not pupa-shaped, or if so, much smaller, 6 mm. or less in length...7

7a Shell elongate, succiniform (Fig. 25, g), very thin; aperture length more than ½ the shell length. *Suborder Heterurethra*........... ....Family SUCCINEIDAE, page 67

7b Shell, when present, elongate (but not succiniform), globose or depressed, and when thin and elongate having a relatively smaller aperture, i.e., less than ½ the shell length....................8

8a Shell rather small, less than 8 mm. in length; pupa-shaped, or when heliciform (Fig. 25, a) or dome-shaped (Fig. 25, b) usually having either ribs or a reflected lip, or when spindle-shaped (Fig. 25, e), being 5 mm. or longer but less than 10 mm. and with a twisted, but not abruptly truncate, columella. *Suborder Orthurethra*..........9

8b Shell minute to large; not pupa-shaped; generally without ribbing when heliciform, without a reflected lip when dome-shaped, and when spindle-shaped with a straight or decidedly truncate columella (see Fig. 13, i, j) and either 5 mm. or less, or 10 mm. or more, in length. *Suborder Sigmurethra*.................................13

9a Shell pupa-shaped (Fig. 25, c)..Family PUPILLIDAE (in part), page 46

9b Shell dome-shaped (Fig. 25, b), spindle-shaped (Fig. 25, e), or heliciform (Fig. 25, a)...10

10a Shell spindle-shaped (Fig. 25, e), imperforate (see Fig. 13, c), very glossy..........................Family CIONELLIDAE, page 43

10b Shell dome-shaped or heliciform, perforate to umbilicate, dull to moderately glossy 11

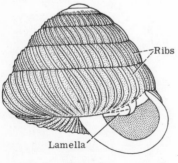

Figure 26

11a Shell with one or more lamellae in the aperture, usually dome-shaped and with rather wide ribs; usually dark brown or reddish-brown (Fig. 26).......Family STROBILOPSIDAE (in part), ...page 65

11b Shell without lamellae in the aperture, usually depressed heliciform (see Fig. 12, n), but without ribs or with rather thin ribs when dome-shaped or globose-heliciform (Fig. 27); usually olive-brown, light tan or white..........12

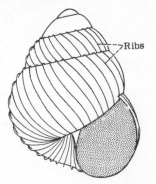

Figure 27

12a Shell depressed, or with ribs when globose (Fig. 27); olive-green, olive-brown, light tan, or white...................................
.......................Family VALLONIIDAE (in part), page 43

12b Shell globose, without ribs (Fig. 28); dark or light reddish-brown....................
......Family PUPILLIDAE (in part), page 46

Figure 28

13a Pedal grooves of the foot conspicuous and well above the angle of the lateral and ventral foot margins (Fig. 29); shell, when present, usually distinctly wider than high, sometimes colored with irregular color markings, but rarely banded; aperture lip not reflected. *Division Aulacopoda* 14

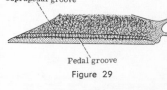

Suprapedal groove

Pedal groove

Figure 29

13b Pedal grooves of the foot inconspicuous and in or close to the angle of the lateral and ventral foot margins (Fig. 30); shell always present, either wider than high or higher than wide, and sometimes marked with color bands; aperture lip may or may not be reflected. *Division Holopoda* 19

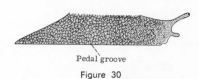

Pedal groove

Figure 30

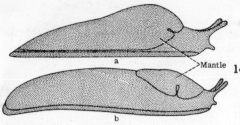

Figure 31

14a Animal without an external shell (Fig. 31)..15

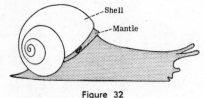

Figure 32

14b Animal with a visible shell (Fig. 32)................17

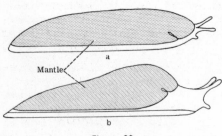

Figure 33

15a Mantle covering nearly the entire back of the animal (Fig. 33)........ ....Family PHILOMYCIDAE, page 69

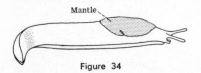

Figure 34

15b Mantle covering only an anterior portion of the animal (Fig. 34)..........16

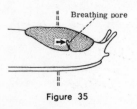

Figure 35

16a Breathing pore in the anterior half of the right side of the mantle (Fig. 35); back never keeled in adults; posterior end rounded when viewed from above ....Family ARIONIDAE, page 72

16b Breathing pore in the posterior half of right
side of mantle (Fig. 36); back keeled (see
Fig. 15), either at posterior end or entirely;
posterior end pointed when viewed from
above........Family LIMACIDAE, page 81

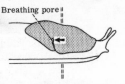

Breathing pore

Figure 36

17a Shell much too small to
cover the contracted ani-
mal (Fig. 37)...........
Family TESTACELLIDAE,
page 119

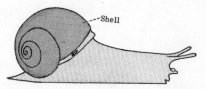

Shell

Figure 37

17b Shell large enough to nearly
or completely conceal the contracted animal (Fig. 38)...18

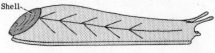

Shell

Figure 38

18a Shell usually opaque, usually dull and with prominent growth
lines or low ribs, umbilicate to widely umbilicate, brown, reddish-
brown, tan or almost white, sometimes with darker reddish color
markings.....................Family ENDODONTIDAE, page 74

18b Shell usually translucent, glossy, smooth or without prominent
growth lines or ribs, narrowly umbilicate, perforate or rarely imperforate, white or light tan-colored to dark olive-brown, often containing some tint of green, but without reddish markings........
....................................Family ZONITIDAE, page 83

19a Shell higher than wide.....................................20

19b Shell wider than high.....................................31

20a Aperture with several lamellae or
teeth; lip reflected (Fig. 39).....21

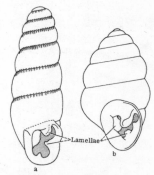

Lamellae

a   b

Figure 39

20b Aperture without lamellae or teeth; lip sharp or reflected......22
21a Shell ribbed, at least near the sutures; shell at least three times higher than wide (Fig. 39, a)....Family **STREPTAXIDAE**, page 120
21b Shell not ribbed; shell height less than three times its width....
..............Family **PUPILLIDAE** (Orthurethra) (in part), page 46
22a Shell urocoptiform (see Fig. 25, d), lip reflected ....
...........................Family **UROCOPTIDAE**, page 127
22b Shell conical (see Fig. 25, h), fusiform (see Fig. 25, e), or bulimoid (see Fig. 25, f); lip may or may not be reflected.............23

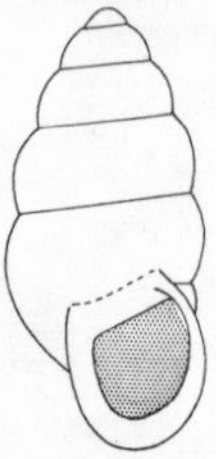

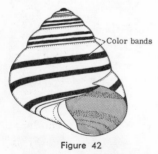

23a Aperture lip reflected (Fig. 40)....................
..Family **PUPILLIDAE** (Orthurethra) (in part), page 46

23b Aperture lip not reflected........................24

Figure 40

24a Shell nearly globose, height barely exceeding the width (Fig. 41) 25
24b Shell elongate, height distinctly exceeding the width..........27

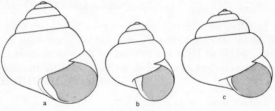

Figure 41

Color bands

25a Shell large, 10 mm. or more in width, usually banded (Fig. 42).......Family **HELMINTHOGLYPTIDAE**, page 182

25b Shell small, 4 mm. or less in width, not banded 26

Figure 42

26a Shell very small, less than 2 mm. in diameter; surface pitted, granulose or striate (see Fig. 11, a (a)(e)(f)), but not ribbed (Fig. 41, b)........Family **PUPILLIDAE** (Orthurethra) (in part), page 46

26b Shell somewhat larger, more than 2 mm. in diameter; surface not pitted, granulose or striate, but usually with fine, low ribs (see Fig. 11, a (c)).........................Family SAGDIDAE, page 134

27a Shell bulimoid (Fig. 43)....................28

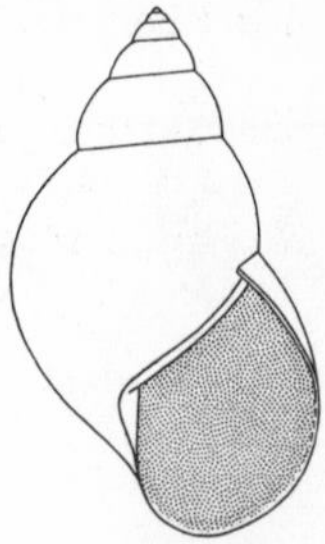

Figure 43

27b Shell conical or fusiform (Fig. 44).........29

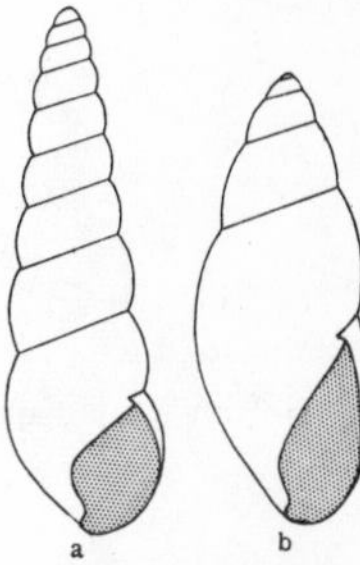

a
Conical

b
Fusiform

Figure 44

28a Shell relatively large, 15 mm. or more in length...............
................................Family BULIMULIDAE, page 130

28b Shell relatively small, 13 mm. or less in length (Fig. 45)
...........Family HELICELLIDAE (in part), page 183

Figure 45

29a Shell without color bands or alternating opaque and translucent bands 30

29b Shell marked with either color bands or alternating transverse opaque and translucent bands (Fig. 45)......................
......................Family HELICELLIDAE (in part), page 183

Figure 46

30a Shell either fusiform and large (more than 20 mm. long), or, if conical, with strongly flattened whorls (Fig. 46)......................
............Family OLEACINIDAE, page 121

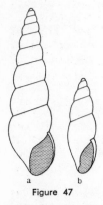

Figure 47

30b Shell either fusiform and small (less than 5 mm. long), or if conical, with rounded whorls (Fig. 47).....Family ACHATINIDAE, page 122

31a Aperture lip not reflected (see Fig. 13, k)......................32
31b Aperture lip reflected (see Fig. 13, l)..........................38
32a Shell large, more than 13 mm. in diameter..................33
32b Shell relatively small, 13 mm. or less in diameter.............36

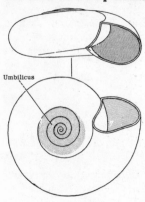

Umbilicus

33a Shell strongly depressed, widely umbilicate (Fig. 48)..........Family HAPLOTREMATIDAE, page 119

Figure 48

33b Shell globose, perforate or imperforate (Fig. 49)..............34

Figure 49

34a Shell very large, more than 30 mm. in diameter; spirally striate
(Fig. 11, a(a)); horn-colored with pale brown bands (Fig. 49, b)....
..........................Family HELICIDAE (in part), page 185

34b Shell smaller, 30 mm. or less in diameter, not spirally striate; white
with dark reddish-brown bands, or white, horn, yellowish or tan
without bands 35

35a Aperture lip thickened and blunt at its edge; shell 20 mm. or
more in diameter, without color bands (Fig. 49, c)..............
.......................Family CAMAENIDAE, page 181

35b Aperture lip sharp, shell 15 mm. or less in diameter, usually with
color bands (Fig. 49, a)..Family HELMINTHOGLYPTIDAE, page 182

36a Shell more than 5 mm. in diameter, sometimes with color bands,
sometimes with carinate whorls (see Fig. 12, r), but without
ribs; aperture lip often thickened within......................
.....................Family HELICELLIDAE (in part), page 183

36b Shell smaller, 5 mm. or less in diameter; sometimes with thin
oblique ribs, but without color bands, carinate whorls, or thickened aperture..37

37a Shell very small, 2 mm. or less in diameter; surface pitted, granulose or striate, but not ribbed (outline as in Fig. 41, b)...........
...........Family PUPILLIDAE (Orthurethra) (in part), page 46

37b Shell somewhat larger, more than 2 mm. in diameter; surface
not pitted, granulose or striate, but often with fine, low ribs.....
.........................Family SAGDIDAE (in part), page 134

38a Shell with dark brown or chestnut color bands................39

38b Shell without dark brown or chestnut color bands...........41

39a Growth lines of shell regularly
spaced and very prominent; aperture lip strongly reflected (Fig. 50)
..Family POLYGYRIDAE, page 136

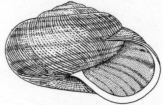

Figure 50

39b Growth lines of shell irregular and not prominent; aperture lip usually not strongly reflected..............................**40**

40a Shell large, more than 16 mm. in diameter; imperforate (Fig. 51)..
...........................**Family HELICIDAE (in part), page 185**

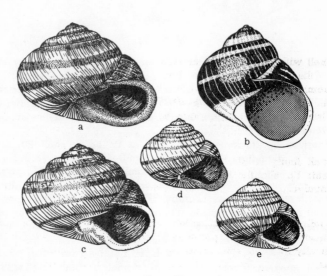

Figure 51

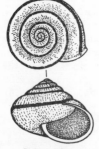

40b Shell smaller, 16 mm. or less in diameter; narrowly umbilicate (Fig. 52)...................
..........**Family BRADYBAENIDAE, page 181**

Figure 52

41a Shell small, 3mm. or less in diameter......................**42**

41b Shell relatively large, more than 5 mm. in diameter...........**43**

42a Shell without lamellae in the aperture; growth lines not prominent; whitish to light tan-colored (Fig. 53)......
.................Family VALLONII-
DAE (Orthurethra) (in part), page 43

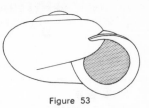

Figure 53

42b Shell with one or more lamellae in the aperture; growth lines prominent; chestnut brown (Fig. 54)....Family STROBILOPSIDAE (Orthurethra) (in part), page 65

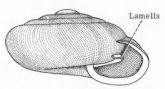

Lamella

Figure 54

43a Shell finely striate, narrowly umbilicate, growth lines not prominent; lip slightly to moderately reflected; whorls often slightly angular.....................Family BRADYBAENIDAE, page 181

43b Shell with or without striae, imperforate to widely umbilicate, growth lines usually prominent; lip often greatly reflected; whorls usually rounded, sometimes strongly angular, but not weakly angular.....................Family POLYGYRIDAE (in part), page 136

PICTURED-KEY TO EASTERN
U.S. LAND SNAIL SPECIES

HELICINIDAE

This is a primitive, mainly tropical family of land operculates. Their shells are usually wider than high and are all imperforate, the umbilical region occupied by a callous pad. The opercula are either paucispiral or concentric and are layered with a rather thin calcareous deposit.

1a Shell small, 3 mm. or less in width or diameter, strongly depressed. Fig. 55.................................*Lucidella tantilla* (Pilsbry)

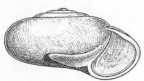

WIDTH: 2-3 mm.* RANGE: Florida.
Shell with about 3½ whorls; faintly yellowish to white. Growth lines prominent. Operculum concentric.

Figure 55. *Lucidella tantilla* (Pilsbry).

1b Shell medium to large, 5 mm. or more in diameter, not depressed, or only moderately depressed....................................2

2a Shell spirally striate; operculum paucispiral. Fig. 56............
....................................*Hendersonia occulta* (Say)

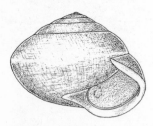

WIDTH: 6-8 mm. RANGE: Pennsylvania, Virginia, North Carolina, Tennessee, Illinois, Wisconsin, Minnesota, Iowa. Shell with 4½-5 whorls; cinnamon red to pale yellow. Periphery slightly angular, sometimes weakly keeled, particularly in younger specimens.

Figure 56. *Hendersonia occulta* (Say).

2b Shell without spiral striae; operculum concentric. Genus *Helicina* 3

*Measurements represent those of the shell unless stated otherwise.

3a Shell relatively large, 9-12 mm. in diameter; spire high (height and diameter almost equal). Fig. 57.......*Helicina chrysocheila* **Binney**

WIDTH: 9-12 mm. RANGE: Texas.
  Shell with about 5 whorls; pale yellow, light pink or white, sometimes with a reddish band.

Figure 57. *Helicina chrysocheila* Binney.

3b Shell of medium size, usually less than 9 mm. in diameter, moderately depressed **4**

4a Body whorl broadly rounded at its periphery. Fig. 58............
....*Helicina orbiculata* **(Say)**

WIDTH: 5-8.5 mm. RANGE: Georgia, Florida, Tennessee, Alabama, Mississippi, Arkansas, Louisiana, Oklahoma.
Shell with about 4½ whorls; white to buff, sometimes pink, often with brownish or white bands. The back of the animal is gray, the foot white.

Figure 58. *Helicina orbiculata* (Say).

4b Body whorl subangular at its periphery. Fig. 59................
....*Helicina clappi* **Pilsbry**

WIDTH: 7-9 mm. RANGE: Florida.
  Shell with 5-5½ whorls; white, pale yellow, or red, sometimes with several red bands. The back of the animal is black, the tentacles gray, and the foot white.

Figure 59. *Helicina clappi* Pilsbry.

POMATIASIDAE

This tropical or subtropical family has snails with elongate shells which are sculptured with many fine ribs. Small calcareous projections at rather regular intervals just below the sutures give them a crenulated appearance. The earlier whorls are usually broken off in the adult stage, making the shell decollate. The shell is umbilicate; the operculum spiral.

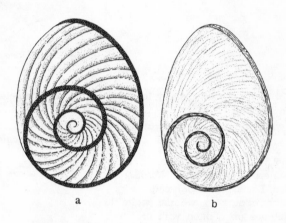

Figure 60. Operculum of a, *Opisthosiphon bahamensis*, showing slanting plates; b, *Chondropoma dentatum*.

1a Shell with an opening for a breathing tube behind the outer lip; without spiral striae; inner edge of aperture sharp. Figs. 60, a; 61 . .
. . . . .*Opisthosiphon bahamensis* (Pfeiffer)

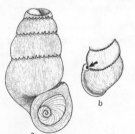

LENGTH: 8-9.5 mm. RANGE: Florida.

Shell with 3-4 whorls remaining in decollated adults; uniform pale tan to dull red, sometimes with interrupted light brown bands. Operculum with a calcareous layer of slanting plates (Fig. 60, a).

Figure 61. *Opisthosiphon bahamensis* (Pfeiffer). a, Apertural view; b, view showing opening for breathing tube.

1b Shell without opening for breathing tube behind the outer lip; spirally striate; inner edge of aperture smooth and rounded. Figs. 60, b; 62
......................................*Chondropoma dentatum* **(Say)**

LENGTH: 10-12 mm. RANGE: Florida.

Shell with about 4 whorls remaining in decollated adults; dull red to light tan, sometimes with several narrow interrupted bands or spots.

Figure 62. *Chondro-poma dentatum* (Say).

TRUNCATELLIDAE

This family is mainly tropical or subtropical in distribution. The shells are very small, cylindrical, imperforate, usually decollate, and often heavily ribbed. The operculum is subspiral (Fig. 63) and corneous with a calcareous layer.

1a Shell with a large, thick, prominent rib behind lip **2**

1b Shell without a more prominent rib behind lip..3

Figure 63. Subspiral operculum of *Truncatella.*

2a Ribs heavy, 15 or less on the last whorl. Fig. 64.................
......................................*Truncatella clathrus* **Lowe**

LENGTH: 4-5 mm. RANGE: Florida.

Shell with 3½-4 whorls remaining in decollated adults; buff to dark reddish-brown. This is the most coarsely ribbed *Truncatella* species in this country.

Figure 64. *Trun-catella clathrus* Lowe.

2b Ribs moderately heavy, 20 or more on the last whorl. Fig. 65....
.....................................*Truncatella bilabiata* Pfeiffer

LENGTH: 4-5 mm. RANGE: Florida.

Shell with 3½-4½ whorls remaining in decollated adults; light tan or pinkish-tan to whitish-gray.
The prominence of the ribs varies greatly, some specimens having ribs as shown in Fig. 67.

Figure 65. *Trunca-
tella bilabiata*
Pfeiffer.

3a Shell without ribs. Fig. 66.......*Truncatella subcylindrica* (Linné)

LENGTH: 5-7 mm. RANGE: Introduced (?) into Rhode
Island.

Shell with 3½-4½ whorls remaining in decollated
adults; pale buff, horn or white.

Figure 66. *Truncatella
subcylindrica* (Lin-
né).

3b Shell completely ribbed, or with ribs only below the suture. Fig.67
.....................................*Truncatella pulchella* Pfeiffer

LENGTH: 5-7.5 mm. RANGE: Florida, Texas.

Shell with 4-4½ whorls remaining in decollated
adults; pale buff to amber-yellow or almost colorless.
The prominence of the ribs varies, some specimens having ribs as shown in Fig. 65.

Figure 67. *Truncatella
pulchella* Pfeiffer.

CARYCHIIDAE

A group of snails with minute, elongate, white shells frequenting moist to wet places, often in rotting logs or on dead leaves in wooded valleys. The eyes are sessile at the bases of the contractile tentacles. Without opercula.

1a Shell longer than 1.75 mm..................................2

1b Shell shorter than 1.75 mm...............................3

2a Whorls rapidly tapering to apex. Fig. 68..*Carychium stygium* Call

LENGTH: 2-2.5 mm. RANGE: Kentucky, Tennessee.
Shell with 5-5½ whorls; white. Sutures rather deeply impressed. Shows the same variation as other carychiids as to presence or absence of a columellar or parietal lamella. This species is an inhabitant of caves.

Figure 68. *Carychium stygium* Call.

2b Whorls gradually tapering to apex. Fig. 69.................
.....................................*Carychium exiguum* (Say)

LENGTH: 1.8-2 mm. RANGE: Newfoundland to Colorado, New Mexico and Alabama.
Shell with about 4½ whorls; white to corneous, somewhat transparent. The columellar axis and partitions are absorbed in the first several whorls, as in other carychiids.

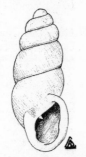

Figure 69. *Carychium exiguum* (Say).

3a Aperture lip greatly thickened. Fig. 70........................
....................................*Carychium floridanum* Clapp

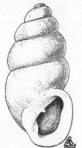

LENGTH: 1.5-1.7 mm. RANGE: South Carolina, Georgia, Florida.

Shell with 4-5 whorls; white. It is larger than *C. nannodes*, but smaller than *C. exiguum* and *C. stygium*. Fine spiral striae may or may not be evident.

Figure 70. *Carychium floridanum* Clapp.

3b Aperture lip relatively thin. Fig. 71..... *Carychium nannodes* Clapp

LENGTH: 1.3-1.5 mm. RANGE: Virginia, West Virginia, Alabama.

Shell with about 4½ whorls; waxy-white, translucent. This is a very minute species. Growth lines are evident only under high magnification.

Figure 71. *Carychium nannodes* Clapp.

VERONICELLIDAE

This is a tropical family of primitive slugs that have their eyes on contractile (not inversible) stalks or tentacles (see Fig. 23). The mantle covers the entire back of the animal and contains neither an external nor internal shell. The lung is posteriorly located, with the breathing pore and excretory openings situated on the underside of the mantle behind the foot. Only one species is native to the United States.

Fig. 72.................................*Veronicella floridana* (Leidy)
LENGTH: 50-70 mm.   RANGE: Florida.

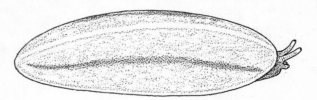

Figure 72. *Veronicella floridana* (Leidy).

42

Animal large, oblong, with rounded back and sharply angular lateral borders. It is ashy to brownish-gray, mottled with black, and has a median whitish line with a long dark longitudinal band on each side about 1/3 the distance to the mantle margin.

CIONELLIDAE

Shells of this family are rather small, elongate, and very glossy. Like most of our land snails, their eyes are situated at the tips of inversible tentacles. This is a Palearctic family, with only one species in the United States.

Fig. 73.....................................*Cionella lubrica* (Müller)

LENGTH: 5-7.5 mm. RANGE: United States, except Georgia, Florida, Texas and California.

Shell with 5½-6 whorls; yellowish-corneous. Very smooth and glossy, almost translucent. The lip is not reflected, but thickened inside the aperture. Columella slightly sinuate.

Figure 73. *Cionella lubrica* (Müller).

VALLONIIDAE

This family has small, usually depressed, but sometimes globose shells, which are often sculptured with fine cuticular ribs. The aperture is toothless.

la Shell globose. Fig. 74....................*Zoögenetes harpa* (Say)

WIDTH: 2.5 mm. RANGE: Maine, New Hampshire, New York, Michigan, Minnesota, Wyoming, Colorado.

Shell with about 4 whorls; olive-green. The first several whorls are nearly smooth, the last two are sculptured with thin cuticular ribs. The lip is thin, not reflected.

Figure 74. *Zoögenetes harpa* (Say).

1b Shell strongly depressed.....................................2

2a Shell relatively thin, brownish; aperture lip thin, sharp and not reflected. Fig. 75.....................*Planogyra asteriscus* (Morse)

Figure 75. *Planogyra asteriscus* (Morse).

WIDTH: 1.7-2 mm. RANGE: Maine, Massachusetts, New York, Michigan.

Shell with about 3½ whorls; pale to dark brown. The first several whorls are nearly smooth, the last sculptured with thin, high cuticular ribs.

2b Shell relatively thick, whitish to light tan; aperture lip thickened and reflected. Genus *Vallonia*...............................3

3a Shell smooth, with only faint growth lines. Fig. 76..............
......................................*Vallonia pulchella* (Müller)

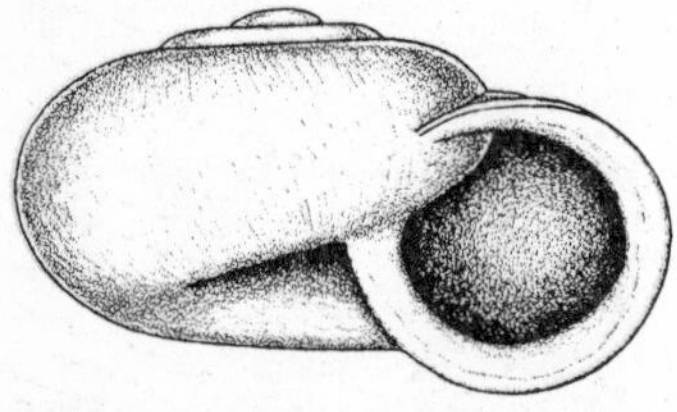

Figure 76. *Vallonia pulchella* (Müller).

WIDTH: 2-2.5 mm. RANGE: North America east of the Rocky Mountains; Canada south to Missouri and Kentucky. Introduced in Texas and California.

Shell with 3-3½ whorls; pale, corneous or white, semi-transparent. This species is easily distinguished because it lacks ribs. It is often found around lawns and gardens.

3b Shell ribbed 4

4a Aperture lip reflected and distinctly or strongly thickened........5

4b Aperture lip reflected but thin...............................7

5a Shell small, diameter 2 mm. or less. Fig. 77...................
....*Vallonia parvula* Sterki

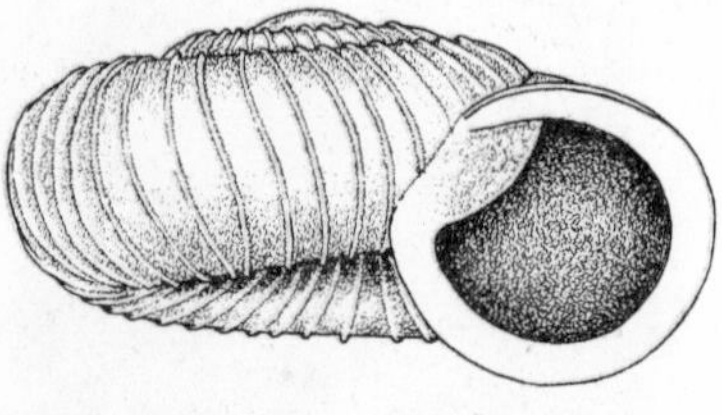

Figure 77. *Vallonia parvula* Sterki.

WIDTH: 1.6-2 mm. RANGE: Ohio, Illinois, Iowa, South Dakota, Kansas, Oklahoma, Texas.

Shell with about 3 whorls; horn to very pale gray or nearly white. Similar to *V. costata* (Fig. 78), but smaller.

5b Shell larger, diameter 2.5 mm. or more........................6

6a 20-35 ribs on the last whorl. Fig. 78........*Vallonia costata* (Müller)

WIDTH: 2.5 mm. RANGE: Michigan, Illinois, Ohio, New York, Maryland, Virginia.

Shell with about 3½ whorls; gray or pale yellowish-corneous. Last whorl descends in front, as in other ribbed species of *Vallonia*.

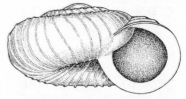

Figure 78. *Vallonia costata* (Müller).

6b 45-60 ribs on the last whorl. Fig. 79..*Vallonia gracilicosta* Reinhardt

WIDTH: 2.5-3 mm. RANGE: Minnesota south to New Mexico, west to California.

Shell with about 3½ whorls; pale tan, corneous, or whitish-gray. Similar to *V. costata*, but with more ribs.

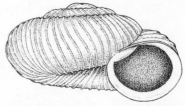

Figure 79. *Vallonia gracilicosta* Reinhardt.

**7a Shell small, diameter 2 mm. or less. Fig. 80.....................
....*Vallonia perspectiva* Sterki**

WIDTH: 2 mm. RANGE: New Jersey south to Alabama, west to Minnesota, Utah and Arizona.

Shell with about 3½ whorls; pale horn to colorless. Shell small, umbilicus wide, ribs delicate, aperture lip continuous.

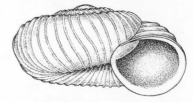

Figure 80. *Vallonia perspectiva* Sterki.

**7b Shell larger, diameter 2.5 mm. or more. Fig. 81.................
......................................*Vallonia cyclophorella* Sterki**

WIDTH: 2.5-3 mm. RANGE: North Dakota south to Texas, west to Oregon and California.

Shell with about 3½ whorls; pale horn, grayish or colorless; translucent. Similar to *V. perspectiva*, but larger and with a relatively narrower umbilicus.

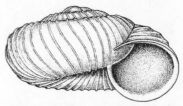

Figure 81. *Vallonia cyclophorella* Sterki.

45

PUPILLIDAE

This is a large family having small to minute, usually pupa-shaped shells (see Fig. 82). It is world-wide in distribution. The shell aperture usually contains several, sometimes many, teeth. Classification and species characters are based mainly on these apertural teeth (see Fig. 83 for terminology).

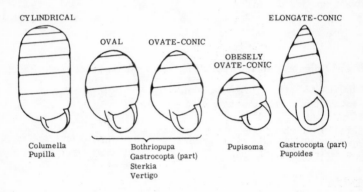

Figure 82. Shell shapes in the Pupillidae.

1a Aperture without teeth (lamellae, folds or plicae)..............2

1b Aperture with teeth. See Fig. 83...............................9

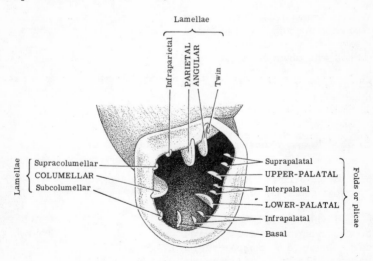

Figure 83. Terminology of pupillid teeth (after Pilsbry).

2a Aperture lip thickened and noticably reflected. **Genus *Pupoides***..3
2b Aperture lip not thickened and not, or only slightly, reflected....4

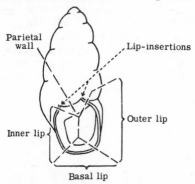

Figure 84. Terminology of aperture and peristome (lip). In this figure the peristome is not complete.

3a Outer lip (see Fig. 84) joined by an angular lamella in the form of a callus. Fig. 85...................*Pupoides albilabris* (Adams)

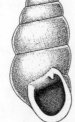

LENGTH: 4.2-5 mm. RANGE: Maine to Florida, west to North Dakota, Colorado and Arizona.
Shell with 6-6½ whorls; medium or dark cinnamon. Spire tapering; aperture oval. Usually coated with dirt.

Figure 85. *Pupoides albilabris* (Adams).

3b No trace of an angular lamella. Fig. 86...*Pupoides modicus* (Gould)

LENGTH: 3.5-4.2 mm. RANGE: Georgia, Florida.
Shell with 4½-5 whorls; dull brown. Smaller, thinner and somewhat more striate than *P. albilabris.*

Figure 86. *Pupoides modicus* (Gould).

4a Shell cylindrical (see Fig. 82)....................................5
4b Shell obesely ovate-conic (see Fig. 82). **Genus Pupisoma**.......7

5a Shell relatively large, 3.2-4 mm. long; sutures moderately impressed. Fig. 87 . . . .*Pupilla muscorum* (Linné)

LENGTH: 3.2-4 mm. RANGE: Northeastern United States to Oregon, south to Arizona and Texas.

Shell with 5½-7½ whorls; brown. Aperture usually toothless, but it sometimes has one or more teeth (see Fig. 108). The palatal fold is small and tubercular in shells with teeth.

Figure 87. *Pupilla muscorum* (Linné).

5b Shell relatively small, 1.5-3 mm. long; sutures deeply impressed. Genus *Columella* 6

6a Cylindrical, but slightly tapering toward the apex. Fig. 88 . . . .
. . . .*Columella edentula* (Draparnaud)

LENGTH: 1.75-2.5 mm. RANGE: Canada south to Virginia, Pennsylvania, Iowa, Montana and Oregon; Alabama.

Shell with 5½-6½ whorls; cinnamon or darker, sometimes with whitish streaks; perforate; thin, glossy and nearly smooth.

Figure 88. *Columella edentula* (Draparnaud).

6b Cylindrical, not tapering. Fig. 89 . . . .*Columella alticola* (Ingersoll)

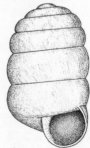

LENGTH: 2.5-3 mm. RANGE: Illinois, Iowa, Kansas, Wyoming, Colorado, New Mexico, Utah, Arizona.

Shell with 6-7 whorls; chestnut-brown, nearly translucent; striate. Whorls rather strongly convex; aperture small.

Figure 89. *Columella alticola* (Ingersoll).

7a Shell surface sculptured with minute spiral striae. Fig. 90......
..............................*Pupisoma dioscoricola* (Adams)

LENGTH: 1.5-2 mm. RANGE: South Carolina,
Georgia, Florida, Alabama, Texas.
Shell with 3½-4 whorls; cinnamon; glossy;
perforate. Columellar lip margin dilated over
the umbilical perforation.

Figure 90. *Pupisoma dioscoricola* (Adams.)

7b Shell surface sculptured with pits and granules................8
8a Umbilicus narrow, one-sixth or less the diameter of the shell. Fig.
91.......................................*Pupisoma minus* Pilsbry

LENGTH: 1.3-1.4 mm. RANGE: South Carolina,
Georgia, Florida.
Shell with about 3½ whorls; cinnamon; rather dull; narrowly umbilicate; globose-conic. Surface without spiral striae.

Figure 91. *Pupisoma minus* Pilsbry (after Pilsbry).

8b Umbilicus wider, about one-fifth the diameter of the shell. Fig.92..
..............................*Pupisoma macneilli* (Clapp)

LENGTH: 1.3 mm. RANGE: South Carolina, Georgia, Alabama.
Shell with about 3½ whorls; chestnut-brown; somewhat glossy; umbilicate. Surface granulated and with faint growth lines, but not striate.

Figure 92. *Pupisoma macneilli* (Clapp).

9a Parietal and angular lamellae converging inward, and more or
less united. Genus *Gastrocopta*..............................10
9b Parietal and angular lamellae separate and distinct when present;
either or both may be lacking..............................21

10a Teeth of parietal wall well-developed.........................11

10b Teeth of parietal wall not well-developed.....................18

11a Palatal folds situated on a white callous ridge; aperture almost filled by the large teeth. Subgenus *Albinula*..................12

11b Palatal folds not on a callus; teeth prominent but not nearly filling aperture. Subgenus *Gastrocopta* s.s......................14

12a Shell relatively large, 3-4.8 mm. long. Fig. 93...................
....*Gastrocopta armifera* (Say)

RANGE: Maine to Florida, west to North Dakota, Colorado and New Mexico.

Shell with 6½-7½ whorls; white; perforate, lightly marked with irregular growth lines. Lip thin, expanded (weakly reflected).

Figure 93. *Gastrocopta armifera* (Say).

12b Shell medium to small, 2.5 mm. or less in length.............13

13a Shell medium, 2.2–2.5 mm. long; angulo-parietal lamellae not forked. Fig. 94.....................*Gastrocopta contracta* (Say)

RANGE: Maine to Florida, west to Mexico.

Shell with about 5½ whorls; white or bluish-white. Spire tapering, irregularly marked with growth lines. Aperture triangular, the angulo-parietal lamella joins the outer lip.

Figure 94. *Gastrocopta contracta* (Say)

13b Shell relatively small, about 1.75 mm. long; angulo-parietal lamella forked in front. Fig. 95 . . . .*Gastrocopta holzingeri* (Sterki)

RANGE: New York to Montana, south to Illinois, Kansas and New Mexico.

Shell with about 5 whorls; white, more or less transparent. Spire rather cylindrical, aperture more or less oval, columellar lamella curving down at the inner end.

Figure 95. *Gastrocopta holzingeri* (Sterki).

14a Lip heavily calloused within **15**

14b Lip thin, not heavily calloused within **17**

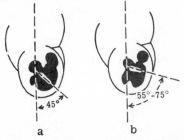

Figure 96. Angles between lower palatal fold and columellar axis in (a) *Gastrocopta rupicola*, and (b) *G. procera* and *G. cristata*.

15a Lower-palatal callus directed at a 45° angle from the columella. Figs. 96, a; 97 . . . .*Gastrocopta rupicola* (Say)

LENGTH: 1.8-2.5 mm. RANGE: South Carolina to Floriday, west to Texas.

Shell with 5½-6 whorls; pale brown, corneous or white. The inner lip of the aperture is conspicuously thickened by a heavy white callus, similar to that of *G. procera* (Fig. 98) and *G. cristata* (Fig. 99). Differs from these by its generally smaller size and by the angle of the lower palatal callus.

Figure 97. *Gastrocopta rupicola* (Say).

15b Lower-palatal callus directed at a 55°-75° angle from the columella. Fig. 96, b **16**

16a Angulo-parietal lamella strongly bifid at the tip. Fig. 98.........
....*Gastrocopta procera* (Gould)

LENGTH: 2.2-3 mm. RANGE: Maryland and South Carolina west to South Dakota and Arizona.

Shell with 5-6 whorls; cinnamon to tannish-brown. In frontal view a distinct spur is evident on the right side of the angulo-parietal lamella.

Figure 98. *Gastrocopta procera* (Gould).

16b Angulo-parietal lamella not bifid. Fig. 99.....................
.....................*Gastrocopta cristata* (Pilsbry and Vanatta)

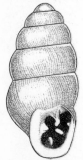

LENGTH: 2.7-3 mm. RANGE: Oklahoma, Texas and Arizona.

Shell with about 5½ whorls; brown. Angulo-parietal lamella not noticeably divided. Columellar lamella strengthened beneath by a low callus.

Figure 99. *Gastrocopta cristata* (Pilsbry and Vanatta).

17a Diameter greater than 1 mm. Fig. 100......................
.................*Gastrocopta riograndensis* (Pilsbry and Vanatta)

LENGTH: 2.5 mm. RANGE: Texas.

Shell with 5-5½ whorls; cinnamon to tannish-brown. Aperture with six teeth, including an infraparietal tooth.

Figure 100. *Gastrocopta riograndensis* (Pilsbry and Vanatta).

52

17b Diameter less than 1 mm. Fig. 101..............................
.... *Gastrocopta pellucida hordeacella* (Pilsbry)

LENGTH: 1.7-2.6 mm. RANGE: New Jersey to Florida,
west to California.

Shell with 5-5½ whorls; pale brown to white; cylindrical. Columellar lamella long and rather stout.

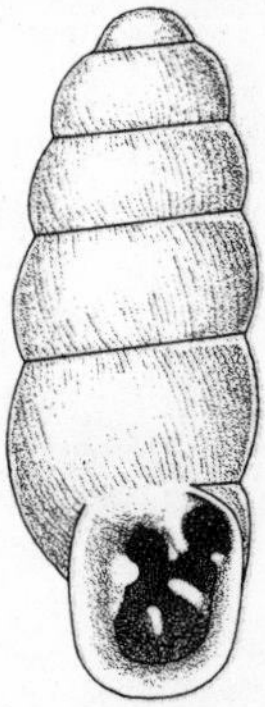

Figure 101. Gastro-
copta pellucida hor-
deacella (Pilsbry).

18a Aperture with palatal folds. Subgenus *Vertigopsis*............19

18b Aperture without palatal folds. Subgenus *Privatula*. Fig. 102....
.......................*Gastrocopta (Privatula) corticaria* (Say)

LENGTH: 2.5 mm. RANGE: Maine west to Minnesota,
south to Florida and Louisiana.

Shell with 5½ whorls; white, translucent. Aperture
dentation very much reduced, with only angulo-parietal and columellar lamellae. Often found crawling
several feet above the ground on trees.

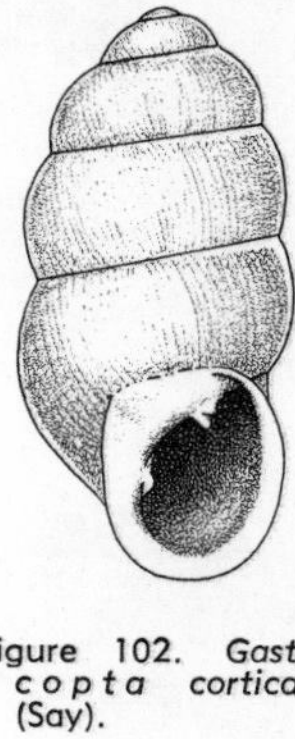

Figure 102. Gastro-
c o p t a corticaria
(Say).

19a Outer lip containing a distinct palatal callus..................20

19b Outer lip without a distinct palatal callus. Fig. 103.............
.....................*Gastrocopta (Vertigopsis) carnegiei* (Sterki)

LENGTH: 1-1.2 mm. RANGE: Ohio.

Shell with 4-4½ whorls; whitish. Lower palatal fold well developed, but not on a callus.

Figure 103. *Gastrocopta carnegiei* (Sterki) (after Pilsbry).

20a Shell ovate-conic. Fig. 104....................................
....................*Gastrocopta (Vertigopsis) tappaniana* (**Adams**)

LENGTH: 1.6-2 mm. RANGE: Maine to Georgia, west to South Dakota, Kansas and Arizona.

Shell with 4-5 whorls; clear corneous, whitish, or gray. Shell usually larger and spire more oval than in *G. pentodon* (Fig. 105).

Figure 104. *Gastrocopta tappaniana* (Adams).

20b Shell elongate-conic. Fig. 105...................................
.......................*Gastrocopta (Vertigopsis) pentodon* (**Say**)

LENGTH: 1.5-1.8 mm. RANGE: Maine to Florida, west to Arizona.

Shell with about 5 whorls; white or corneous, transparent. Spire tapering; angulo-parietal lamella simple.

Figure 105. *Gastrocopta pentodon* (Say).

21a Angular lamella long, emerging to the lip-insertion (see Fig. 84).
Genus *Sterkia*. Fig. 106...........*Sterkia eyriesi rhoadsi* (Pilsbry)

LENGTH: 1.8-1.9 mm. RANGE: Florida.
Shell with 4½-5 whorls; clay color; glossy; ovate.
Aperture with 5 teeth. Lower palatal fold long and
deeply placed within the aperture.

Figure 106. *Sterkia eyriesi rhoadsi* (Pilsbry).

21b Angular lamella absent, or if present, either short or not near the
lip-insertion 22
22a Shell cylindrical (see Fig. 82), 2.8-6 mm. long. Genus *Pupilla*....23
22b Shell oval to ovate-conic (see Fig. 82), 1.5-3 mm. long.........24
23a Palatal fold elongate. Fig. 107..............*Pupilla blandi* Morse

LENGTH: 3-3.4 mm. RANGE: North Dakota to Texas,
west to Montana, Nevada and New Mexico.
Shell with 6-6½ whorls; light brown; cylindrical.
Aperture with columellar, parietal and palatal teeth. The
palatal fold is always well-developed.

Figure 107. *Pupilla blandi* Morse.

23b Palatal fold, when present, tubercular. Fig. 108...............
.....................................*Pupilla muscorum* (Linné)

LENGTH: 2.8-4 mm. RANGE: Northeastern United
States to Oregon, south to Arizona and Texas.
Shell with 5½-7½ whorls; brown. Aperture without teeth, or when teeth are present, the palatal fold
is small and tubercular.

Figure 108. *Pupilla muscorum* (Linné).

24a Shell surface pitted or granulose. Genus Bothriopupa. Fig. 109..
.... *Bothriopupa variolosa* **(Gould)**

LENGTH: 1.7-1.8 mm. RANGE: Florida.

Shell with about 4½ whorls; pale tan, opaque. Aperture with 3 teeth. Columellar lamella and palatal fold rather poorly developed. Outer lip indented.

Figure 109. *Bothriopupa variolosa* (Gould). S u r f a c e pits and granules not shown.

24b Shell surface smooth or striate. Genus Vertigo................25
25a Inner end of the columellar lamella turning downward; lower-palatal fold unusually long. Subgenus Angustula. Fig. 110......
.... *Vertigo (Angustula) milium* **(Gould)**

LENGTH: 1.4-1.8 mm. RANGE: Maine to Florida, west to South Dakota and Arizona.

Shell with 4½-5 whorls; pale brown or cinnamon. Shell ovate-conic, glossy, weakly striate. Aperture with 6 teeth; outer (palatal) lip indented, as in most other Vertigos.

Figure 110. *Vertigo milium* (Gould).

25b Inner end of the columellar lamella not turning downward; lower-palatal fold not excessively long..............................26
26a Columellar lamella almost vertical. Subgenus Vertillaria. Fig. 111
.... *Vertigo (Vertillaria) oscariana* **Sterki**

LENGTH: 1.4-1.6 mm. RANGE: Virginia and West Virginia, south to Florida, west to Arkansas and Texas.

Shell with 4½-5 whorls; pale horn. Aperture with 3 teeth. Columellar lamella blunt and thick, palatal fold short, thick and set deeply within the aperture.

Figure 111. *Vertigo oscariana* Sterki.

26b Columellar lamella almost horizontal. Subgenus *Vertigo* s. s...
....**27, 34, 37**

The Eastern species of the Subgenus *Vertigo*, s. s., fall into five groups, the *V. ovata* group, the *V. pygmaea* group, the *V. tridentata* group, the *V. gouldi* group, and the *V. modesta* group. The members of these groups which occur in the Eastern United States are illustrated in Fig. 112.

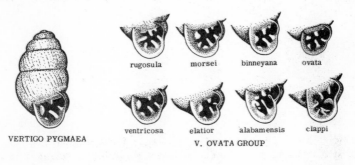

VERTIGO PYGMAEA

rugosula   morsei   binneyana   ovata

ventricosa   elatior   alabamensis   clappi

V. OVATA GROUP

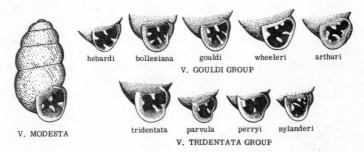

V. MODESTA

hebardi   bollesiana   gouldi   wheeleri   arthuri

V. GOULDI GROUP

tridentata   parvula   perryi   nylanderi

V. TRIDENTATA GROUP

Figure 112. Apertural characters of species of the Subgenus *Vertigo*.

VERTIGO PYGMAEA GROUP

Fig. 113...............................**Vertigo pygmaea (Draparnaud)**

LENGTH: 1.8-2 mm. RANGE: Maine to Ohio, south to Virginia.

Shell with 5 whorls; auburn or chestnut-brown. The last whorl has a strong, light-colored crest a short distance behind the lip. Aperture truncate basally.

Figure 113. *Vertigo pygmaea* (Draparnaud).

VERTIGO MODESTA GROUP

Fig. 114......................................*Vertigo modesta* (Say)

LENGTH: 2.2-2.7 mm. RANGE: Northern United States from Maine to California; New Mexico, Arizona.

Shell with 4½-5½ whorls; dark olive-brown to chestnut brown. Growth lines prominent. Aperture with four short teeth arranged in the form of a cross. Occasionally with only three teeth, or five.

Figure 114. *Vertigo modesta* (Say).

KEY TO *VERTIGO OVATA* GROUP

27a Shell with well-developed striae. Fig. 115...*Vertigo rugosula* Sterki

LENGTH: 1.7-2 mm. RANGE: South Carolina to Florida, west to Oklahoma and Texas.

Shell with 4½-5 whorls; chestnut-brown. Palatal lip only slightly indented.

Figure 115. *Vertigo rugosula* Sterki.

27b Shell with very weak striae................................**28**
28a Peristome usually deeply constricted in palatal region.......**29**
28b Peristome usually only moderately or slightly constricted in pala- tal region **30**
29a Parietal and angular lamellae about equal in size. Fig. 116.... ....*Vertigo clappi* Brooks and Hunt

LENGTH: 1.5 mm. RANGE: West Virginia.

Shell with about 5½ whorls; pale brown. Aperture with 6 teeth. The palatal folds are distinctly different from those in any other *Vertigo*. Aperture basally truncate.

Figure 116. *Vertigo clappi* Brooks and Hunt (after Pilsbry).

29b Parietal lamella much larger than angular lamella. Fig. 117....
.......................................*Vertigo alabamensis* Clapp

LENGTH: 1.5-1.8 mm. RANGE: Alabama.
  Shell with about 5½ whorls; light brown. The palatal folds and columellar lamellae are strongly developed.

Figure 117. *Vertigo alabamensis* Clapp.

30a Shell relatively large, over 2.5 mm. long. Fig. 118............
...*Vertigo morsei* Sterki

LENGTH: 2.7-3 mm. RANGE: New York and New Jersey to Michigan, Indiana and Illinois.
  Shell with 6-6½ whorls; auburn to chestnut-brown; large. The aperture is relatively small, typically with 8 or 9 teeth.

Figure 118. *Vertigo morsei* Sterki.

30b Shell relatively small, less than 2.5 mm. long................31
31a Shell nearly oval in outline................................32
31b Shell longer, ovate-conic to almost elongate-conic...........33
32a Aperture with 6-9 teeth. Fig. 119..............*Vertigo ovata* Say

LENGTH: 2.2-2.3 mm. RANGE: Maine to Florida, west to Oregon and California.
  Shell with 4½-5 whorls; auburn or dark brown. Last whorl relatively large. Palatal folds and columellar lamellae well-developed.

Figure 119. *Vertigo ovata* Say.

32b Aperture with 4 or 5 teeth. Fig. 120....*Vertigo ventricosa* (Morse)

LENGTH: 1.7-2 mm. RANGE: New England to Ohio, Michigan and Illinois.

Shell with 4-4½ whorls; auburn. Aperture semicircular, teeth not especially well-developed.

Figure 120. *Vertigo ventricosa* (Morse).

33a Spire tapering from body whorl to apex. Fig. 121..............
..*Vertigo elatior* Sterki

LENGTH: 2.1-2.2 mm. RANGE: Maine.

Shell with about 5 whorls; tan to cinnamon. Aperture typically with five teeth.

Figure 121. *Vertigo elatior* Sterki.

33b Body whorl and penultimate whorl of about the same diameter.
Fig. 122................................*Vertigo binneyana* Sterki

LENGTH: 2.1 mm. RANGE: Iowa, Montana, New Mexico.

Shell with about 5 whorls; auburn. Aperture elongate, typically with six teeth.

Figure 122. *Vertigo binneyana* Sterki.

KEY TO *VERTIGO TRIDENTATA* GROUP

34a Lower-palatal lamella situated deep within the aperture. Fig. 123.
....*Vertigo nylanderi* Sterki

LENGTH: 1.6-1.7 mm. RANGE: Maine.
   Shell with 4½-5 whorls; cinnamon. Growth lines prominent. Aperture with 6 teeth. Angular and subcolumellar lamellae not well developed.

Figure 123. *Vertigo nylanderi* Sterki.

34b Lower-palatal lamella situated near the lip...................**35**

35a Shell relatively large, 1.8-2.3 mm. long; upper-palatal lamella present, but very small. Fig. 124.........*Vertigo tridentata* Wolf

RANGE: Maine to West Virginia, west to Minnesota, Kansas and Texas.
   Shell with about 5 whorls, yellowish. Aperture rather narrow, with 3 white teeth.

Figure 124. *Vertigo tridentata* Wolf.

35b Shell relatively small, about 1.5 mm. long; upper-palatal lamella usually absent **36**

36a Shell nearly oval in outline; yellowish. Fig. 125..............
....*Vertigo parvula* Sterki

LENGTH: 1.4-1.6 mm. RANGE: Ohio, Virginia, Tennessee and North Carolina.

Shell with about 5 whorls; yellowish. Aperture rather narrow, with 3 white teeth.

Figure 125. *Vertigo parvula* Sterki (after Pilsbry).

36b Shell ovate-conic to almost conic; dark olive-buff. Fig. 126......
....*Vertigo perryi* Sterki

LENGTH: 1.5-1.6 mm. RANGE: Rhode Island and Massachusetts.

Shell with about 4½ whorls. Aperture broad, usually with 3, sometimes with 4, brownish teeth.

Figure 126. *Vertigo perryi* Sterki.

KEY TO *VERTIGO GOULDI* GROUP

37a Columellar lamella with a convex callus against its lower side; outer lip with a strong palatal callus. Fig. 127...............
...................................*Vertigo arthuri* von Martens

LENGTH: 1.6-1.7 mm. RANGE: North Dakota.

Shell with about 5 whorls; brown. Aperture rather small and triangular. Outer lip with a heavy inner callus.

Figure 127. *Vertigo arthuri* von Martens (after Pilsbry).

37b Columellar lamella without a callus; outer lip without a strong palatal callus 38

38a Northern and Northeastern species..........................39

38b Southern species (Gulf States).............................40

39a Striae well developed. Fig. 128..........*Vertigo gouldi* (Binney)

LENGTH: 1.5-2.1 mm. RANGE: Maine and Michigan to Montana, south to Illinois, Colorado and Arizona.

Shell with 4½-5½ whorls; light brown to chestnut-brown. Growth lines prominent. Aperture with 5, rarely 6, teeth. Parietal lamella and palatal folds well-developed.

Figure 128. *Vertigo gouldi* (Binney).

39b Striae weak. Fig. 129.................*Vertigo bollesiana* (Morse)

LENGTH: 1.5 mm. RANGE: Maine, Massachusetts, New Hampshire and New York.

Shell with 4½-5 whorls; amber-brown to light cinnamon. Growth lines prominent. Aperture with five teeth.

Figure 129. *Vertigo bollesiana* (Morse).

40a Shell relatively large, 1.5-1.6 mm. long; cinnamon-colored. Fig. 130.....................................*Vertigo wheeleri* Pilsbry

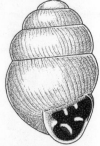

RANGE: Alabama.

Shell with about 4½ whorls; cinnamon. Growth lines prominent. Aperture with five teeth.

Figure 130. *Vertigo wheeleri* Pilsbry.

40b Shell relatively small, about 1.25 mm. long; corneous. Fig. 131...
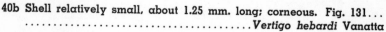......................................*Vertigo hebardi* Vanatta

RANGE: Florida Keys.

Shell with about 4 whorls; corneous; glossy; almost smooth. Aperture with 4 or 5 teeth. Sometimes an angular lamella is present.

Figure 131. *Vertigo hebardi* Vanatta (after Vanatta).

STROBILOPSIDAE

The snails of this family have small, usually ribbed, dome-shaped shells. The shell aperture contains one or more lamellae or folds, the terminology of which is given in Fig. 132. These snails are usually found on decaying and dead leaves in moderately humid forests.

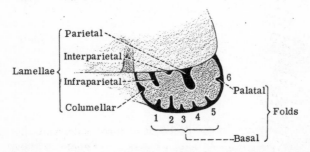

Figure 132. Terminology of strobilopsid teeth (after Pilsbry). Only the parietal lamellae are usually seen in frontal view in mature shells.

1a Shell dome-shaped, globose to slightly depressed; ribs well-developed; umbilicus 1/12-1/6 the diameter of the shell.............2

1b Shell rather strongly depressed, weakly ribbed; umbilicus 1/4-1/3 the diameter of the shell. Fig. 133......*Strobilops hubbardi* Brown

WIDTH: 2.6 mm. RANGE: Georgia, Florida, Mississippi and Texas.
Shell with about 4½ whorls; light chestnut-brown; glossy. Sometimes shouldered. Rather widely umbilicate.

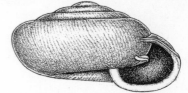

Figure 133. *Strobilops hubbardi* Brown.

2a Spire elevated, convexly conic or high dome-shaped; periphery of last whorl round or subangular............................3

2b Spire less elevated, its sides only slightly convex; periphery of body whorl angular. Fig. 134.................*Strobilops aenea* Pilsbry

WIDTH: 2.4-2.8 mm. RANGE: Massachusetts to Michigan, Illinois and Arkansas, south to Florida and Louisiana.
Shell with about 5½ whorls; light to dark brown; moderately depressed. Narrowly umbilicate. Base somewhat flattened below the periphery.

Figure 134. *Strobilops aenea* Pilsbry.

3a Shell small, diameter 2.5 mm. or less; basal folds very unequal...4
3b Shell larger, diameter 2.75 mm. or more; basal folds nearly equal. Fig. 135.................................*Strobilops affinis* Pilsbry

WIDTH: 2.75-2.8 mm. RANGE: Massachusetts to Minnesota and Kansas, south to Alabama and Oklahoma.

Shell with about 6 whorls; brown. Moderately umbilicate. Spire slightly less convex than S. *labyrinthica* (Fig. 137).

Figure 135. *Strobilops affinis* Pilsbry.

4a Ribs well developed on base of shell. Fig. 136...................
........................*Strobilops texasiana* (Pilsbry and Ferriss)

WIDTH: 1.9-2 mm. RANGE: Virginia to Florida; Alabama, Arkansas, Louisiana, Oklahoma and Texas.

Shell with about 5½ whorls; light brown. Moderately umbilicate. First several whorls smooth. Parietal callus well-developed.

Figure 136. *Strobilops texasiana* (Pilsbry and Ferriss).

4b Ribs absent or only poorly developed on base of shell. Fig. 137...
....................................*Strobilops labyrinthica* (Say)

WIDTH: 2.3-2.5 mm. RANGE: Maine to Minnesota, Kansas and Arkansas, south to Georgia and Alabama.

Shell with about 5½ whorls; chestnut-brown. Narrowly umbilicate. Aperture roundly- to ovate-lunate, lip reflected.

Figure 137. *Strobilops labyrinthica* (Say).

CERIONIDAE

This is a tropical and subtropical family restricted to this hemisphere, and represented by only one species (*Cerion incanum*) in the United States. The shell is large, solid, and pupilliform. It is confined to the sea coast above the high tide level.

Fig. 138.....................................*Cerion incanum* (Binney)

LENGTH: 20-40 mm. RANGE: Florida.

Shell with 9-12 whorls; white, sometimes with a faint bluish tint, or pale gray, sometimes marked with brown stripes.

Figure 138. *Cerion incanum* (Binney).

SUCCINEIDAE

The shells of snails belonging to this primitive family of land pulmonates are very thin, and often amber-colored. These snails are sometimes referred to as the "amber snails." The shell has an unusually large aperture. They are nearly always found close to bodies of water, along stream banks, at the edges of ponds or lakes, and in or near marshes. About twenty species have been recorded in the Eastern United States, but identification is difficult and future much needed revisions will rest mainly on anatomical characters, such as genitalia. Three genera are recognized in the United States: *Succinea*, *Oxyloma*, and *Catinella* and only one typical species is given for each genus by way of example.

1a Shell relatively small, generally 11 mm. or less in length, dull; spire long, almost as long as the shell aperture. Fig. 139..*Catinella*

LENGTH: 7-13 mm. RANGE: New Jersey, North Carolina, Washington, Oregon.

Shell with 2½-3½ whorls; pale yellow-olive; very thin. Aperture elongate-ovate, lip sharp.

Figure 139. *Catinella avara* (Say).

1b Shell larger, generally 12 mm. or more in length, glossy; spire considerably shorter than the shell aperture...................2

2a Margin of genital aperture noticably swollen (Fig. 140, a); shell aperture usually ovate. Fig. 140, b.....................*Succinea*
LENGTH: 6-26 mm. RANGE: United States generally.

Shell with 2½-4½ whorls; pale horn, gray, greenish-yellow to pinkish-white; very thin. Aperture ovate, lip sharp.

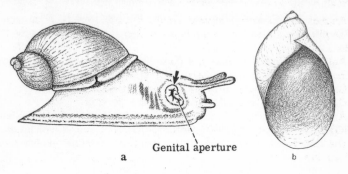

Genital aperture

a
b

Figure 140. *Succinea ovalis* Say.

2b Margin of genital aperture not swollen (Fig. 141, a); shell aperture usually narrowly ovate. Fig. 141, b.................*Oxyloma*
LENGTH: 7.5-20 mm. RANGE: United States generally.

Shell with 2½-4½ whorls; pale horn, yellow to reddish-yellow; very thin. Aperture ovate, lip sharp.

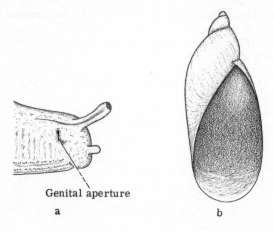

Genital aperture

a
b

Figure 141. *Oxyloma retusa* (Lea).

PHILOMYCIDAE

This family of aulacopod slugs, related to the Arionidae, is found only in the East American Division in this country, but its distribution includes part of Canada, humid temperate and tropical Latin and South America, and parts of the Orient. It has been introduced in Hawaii. The philomycids differ from other stylommatophoran slugs of the United States by the long mantle which covers their entire back. A large shell sac is located inside the mantle, but there is no shell.

1a Animal in general relatively small, usually less than 30 mm. in length; mantle not covering head region (Fig. 33, b). Genus *Pallifera* 2
1b Animal relatively large, more than 50 mm. in length; mantle covering entire body (see Fig. 33, a). Genus *Philomycus*...............9
2a Ground color of animal black, gray, or ashy blue...............3
2b Ground color of animal white, light tan, or buff.................5
3a Animal black. Fig. 142................*Pallifera hemphilli* (Binney)
LENGTH: 25-30 mm. RANGE: North Carolina, Georgia, Michigan.

The dull black of the back fades at the lower edges of the mantle and on the foot.

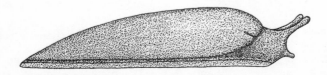

Figure 142. *Pallifera hemphilli* (Binney).

3b Animal ashy-blue or gray; mantle usually with darker pigmented areas 4
4a Animal ashy-blue, with or without an interrupted black line down the center of the mantle; sole of foot white. Fig. 143...........
....*Pallifera dorsalis* (Binney)
LENGTH: 6.5-15 mm. RANGE: Maine to Virginia, west to Michigan and Illinois.

An inhabitant of humid woods, this species is usually found under bark or in soil and humus beneath decaying logs.

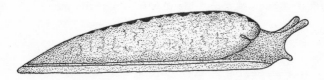

Figure 143. *Pallifera dorsalis* (Binney).

4b Animal gray or brownish gray, with dense darker mottlings on the mantle; margin of foot reddish brown. Fig. 144...................
....*Pallifera varia* Hubricht
LENGTH: 50-65 mm. RANGE: Virginia.

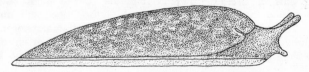

Figure 144. *Pallifera varia* Hubricht.

5a Mantle with two (sometimes three) uninterrupted dark gray-brown longitudinal pigment bands and oblique rows of pigment spots; color pale buff. Fig. 145.....................*Pallifera mutabilis* Hubricht
LENGTH: 60-100 mm. RANGE: Maryland, Virginia, West Virginia, North Carolina, South Carolina, Tennessee, Louisiana, Illinois, Missouri. Margins of the foot olive-gray.

Figure 145. *Pallifera mutabilis* Hubricht.

5b Mantle without uninterrupted longitudinal pigment bands or oblique rows of pigment spots...6
6a Pigmented spots on mantle arranged in transverse bands. Fig. 146.
....*Pallifera wetherbyi* Binney
LENGTH: 10-15 mm. RANGE: Kentucky.

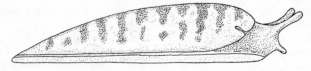

Figure 146. *Pallifera wetherbyi* Binney.

6b Pigmented spots on mantle not in transverse bands..............7
7a Mantle only very slightly pigmented; color light tan (sometimes grayish). Fig. 147......................*Pallifera ohioensis* (Sterki)
LENGTH: 15-30 mm. RANGE: Ohio.
There is a tinge of red at the anterior tip of the foot.

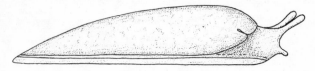

Figure 147. *Pallifera ohioensis* (Sterki).

7b Mantle profusely mottled or distinctly spotted....................**8**

8a Animal buff, profusely mottled with dark gray; markings sparse near mantle edges. Fig. 148....*Pallifera hemphilli marmorea* **Pilsbry**
LENGTH: 20-30 mm. RANGE: Missouri, Louisiana.

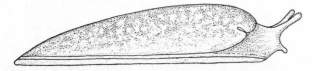

Figure 148. *Pallifera hemphilli marmorea* Pilsbry.

8b Animal white or flesh-colored, with distinct black spots (not mottled); spots often more profuse at mantle edges. Fig. 149........
....*Pallifera fosteri* **Baker**
LENGTH: 15-25 mm. RANGE: Maryland, Virginia, North Carolina, South Carolina, Georgia, Illinois, Missouri.
The mantle is slightly humped in front, and the neck and head are slightly longer than in most other *Pallifera* species.

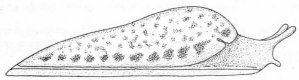

Figure 149. *Pallifera fosteri* Baker.

9a Mantle uniformly mottled with brown, or more usually, with one or two longitudinal rows of black or brown spots running down center of mantle. Fig. 150........*Philomycus carolinianus* **(Bosc)**
LENGTH: 50-100 mm. RANGE: Maine to Florida, west to Iowa and Texas.
Ground color cinnamon-buff to olive-brown. Usually found under the loosened bark of partially decayed logs in humid forests.

Figure 150. *Philomycus carolinianus* (Bosc).

9b Mantle with a dense uninterrupted longitudinal band down its center and a thinner longitudinal band on each side near the mantle edge; longitudinal bands connected by oblique bands. Fig. 151....................................*Philomycus virginicus* Hubricht
LENGTH: 50-100 mm. RANGE: Virginia.

Figure 151. *Philomycus virginicus* Hubricht.

ARIONIDAE

Members of this family of slugs found in the Eastern United States have been introduced from Europe. The family is native to Western North America, Asia, Europe and Africa. Arionid slugs live only in regions of moderate or high humidity, and in the Eastern U.S.A. are found only in the northern states. They are easily distinguished from other slugs because the mantle covers only the anterior part of the body, and their breathing pore is in the anterior half of the mantle.

1a Sides of body without dark longitudinal bands; animal large, more than 70 mm. when extended. Fig. 152...........*Arion ater* (Linné)
LENGTH: 75-150 mm.* RANGE: Introduced into Maine, Michigan, Oregon.
Dark brown, black or red. A large and bulky animal, with coarse long tubercles on its sides and back.

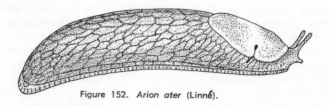

Figure 152. *Arion ater* (Linné).

1b Sides of body usually with dark longitudinal bands; animal smaller, 60 mm. or less when extended.................................2

*Measurements given for members of this family refer to the animal rather than to the internal shell.

2a Body wrinkles conically-pointed when the animal is contracted; reproductive pore immediately below breathing pore. Fig. 153....
.....................................*Arion intermedius* (Normand)
LENGTH: 10-20 mm. RANGE: Introduced into New York, California.

Yellow to shades of gray; sometimes without color bands. There is usually a longitudinal row of dark dots on the front part of the foot margin.

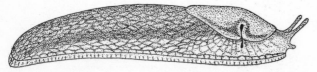

Figure 153. *Arion intermedius* (Normand).

2b Body wrinkles oval to elongate and not conically-pointed when the animal is contracted; reproductive pore in front or behind, but not immediately below breathing pore............................**3**
3a Breathing pore below right mantle pigment band; reproductive pore in front of breathing pore; sole of foot porcelain white; mucus clear. Fig. 154...........................*Arion fasciatus* (Nilsson)
LENGTH: 25-35 mm. RANGE: Introduced into Maine, Massachusetts, New York, Pennsylvania, Washington, D. C., Michigan, Indiana, Illinois, Wisconsin, California.

Pale creamy-gray, darker dorsally. The mantle is granulate, not concentrically wrinkled.

Figure 154. *Arion fasciatus* (Nilsson)

3b Breathing pore in right mantle pigment band; reproductive pore behind breathing pore; sole of foot yellow or orange; mucus yellow or orange..**4**
4a Body color yellowish-gray to bluish-gray; foot bright yellow or orange. Fig. 155........................*Arion hortensis* Férussac
LENGTH: 25-40 mm. RANGE: Introduced into Pennsylvania, Washington, California.

Posterior end rounded (when viewed from above), its mucous pore conspicuous. The suprapedal groove is indistinct.

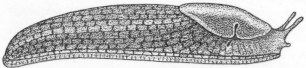

Figure 155. *Arion hortensis* Férussac.

4b Body color grayish-yellow to dark reddish-brown; foot pale yellow. Fig. 156 . . . . *Arion subfuscus* (Draparnaud)
LENGTH: 50-60 mm. RANGE: Introduced into Massachusetts, New York, Pennsylvania.
Smaller and less bulky than *A. ater*. Foot fringe narrow, orange-yellow with vertical gray lines.

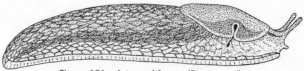

Figure 156. *Arion subfuscus* (Draparnaud).

ENDODONTIDAE

This family is of world-wide distribution and comprises shells exhibiting a great range in size, from minute (*Punctum*) to large (*Anguispira*). The shells are generally umbilicate; are either globose, depressed or discoidal; and are often ribbed (e.g. *Discus*), sometimes lirate (e.g. *Helicodiscus*).

1a Shell large, 9 mm. or more in diameter. Genus *Anguispira* 2

1b Shell smaller, 8 mm. or less in diameter 5

2a Shell periphery acutely carinate. Fig. 157 . . . .
. . . .*Anguispira cumberlandiana* (Lea)

WIDTH: 15-22 mm. RANGE: Tennessee, Alabama.
Shell with 5-6 whorls; pale olive-buff to pale tan, with reddish-brown blotches; lens-shaped. Umbilicus about 1/5 the shell diameter.

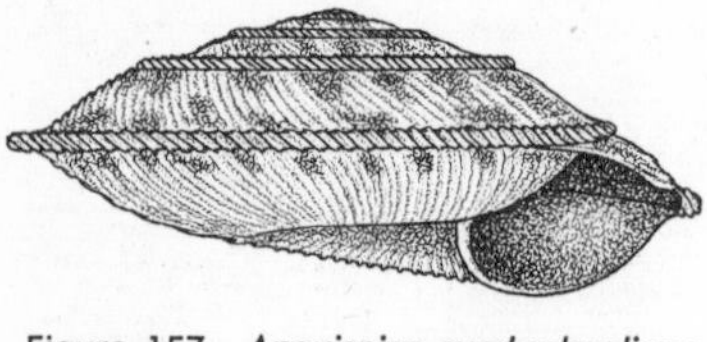

Figure 157. *Anguispira cumberlandiana* (Lea).

2b Shell periphery rounded or angular, but not carinate 3

3a Shell marked with darker reddish-brown bands. Fig.158 . . . .
. . . .*Anguispira kochi* (Pfeiffer)

WIDTH: 17-31 mm. RANGE: Pennsylvania and Kentucky, west to Washington and Oregon.
Shell with about 6 whorls; ground color yellow or tan; large, globose to slightly depressed. Umbilicus 1/5 to 1/3 the diameter of the shell.

Figure 158. *Anguispira kochi* (Pfeiffer).

3b Shell marked with darker reddish-brown blotches..............4
4a Shell 15 mm. or more in diameter. Fig. 159....................
......................................*Anguispira alternata* (Say)

WIDTH: 15-30 mm. RANGE: Pennsylvania to Alabama, west to South
Dakota and Texas.

Shell with 4½-6½ whorls; ground
color yellow or horn; globose to moderately depressed. Umbilicus 1/5 to
1/4 the shell diameter. Periphery
round or angular.

Figure 159. *Anguispira alternata* (Say).

4b Shell 10 mm. or less in diameter. Fig. 160.....................
......................................*Anguispira clarki* Vanatta

WIDTH: 9-10 mm. RANGE: Maryland.
Shell with about 5 whorls; ground
color grayish-yellow; small. Periphery slightly angular.

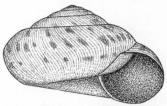

Figure 160. *Anguispira clarki* Vanatta (after Vanatta).

**5a Shell usually medium to small (diameter 2-8 mm.), but when minute
(adult shells less than 2 mm. in diameter) the shell surface is smooth
and without sculpturing of major and minor riblets.............6**

**5b Shell minute (less than 2 mm. in diameter), surface sculptured with
major and minor riblets (Fig. 176). Genus *Punctum*..............19**

6a Shell distinctly ribbed, not lirate. Genus *Discus*.................7

**6b Shell lirate, smooth, or with faint growth lines, but not ribbed. Genus
Helicodiscus 14**

7a Periphery of last whorl rounded..............................8

**7b Periphery of last whorl either angular, flattened, or concave with
single or double carinae.......................................11**

8a Shell with darker brown or reddish-brown spots. Fig. 161........
......................................*Discus rotundatus* (Müller)

WIDTH: 6 mm. RANGE: Introduced into Massachusetts, New
York, New Jersey.

Shell with 6 whorls; ground color
yellowish-brown. The pheriphery
of the last whorl is sometimes subangular and slightly shouldered
(see Fig. 165).

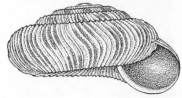

Figure 161. *Discus rotundatus* (Müller).

8b Shell uniform in color; without darker spots....................9

9a Shell with relatively large, coarse ribs (3-4 ribs per mm. on body whorl). Fig. 162.........................*Discus patulus* (Deshayes)

WIDTH: 7-8 mm. RANGE: New York to Florida, west to Iowa and Arkansas.

Shell with about 5½ whorls; cinnamon-brown, with a lighter base. Umbilicus wider (over ½ the shell diameter) than in any other *Discus* species, except *D. bryanti* (Fig. 168) and *D. clappi* (Fig. 167).

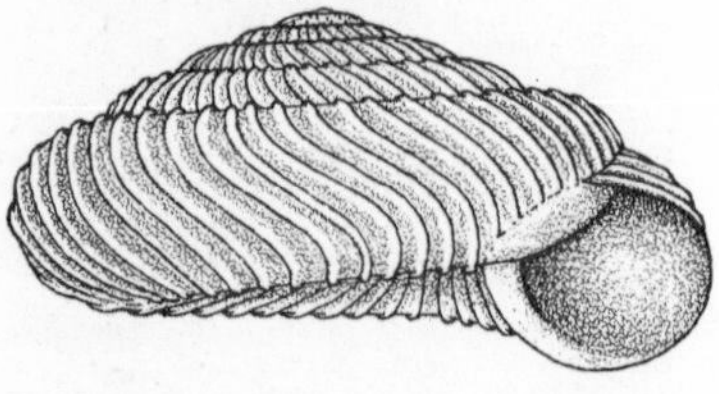

Figure 162. *Discus patulus* (Deshayes).

9b Shell with relatively small, fine ribs (6-8 ribs per mm. on body whorl) 10

10a Shell tightly coiled (adults 6-8 mm. in diameter have 5-6 whorls); ribs indistinct on base of shell. Fig. 163......................
....*Discus macclintocki* (Baker)

WIDTH: 6-8 mm. RANGE: Illinois, Iowa.

Shell with about 6 whorls; horn. High spired, almost dome-shaped. Body whorl flatly rounded.

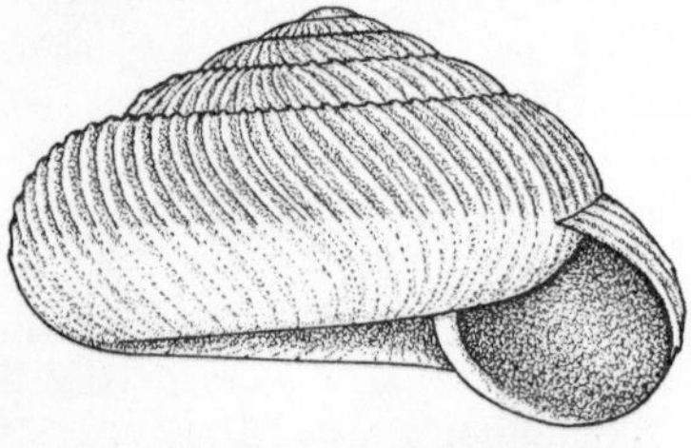

Figure 163. *Discus macclintocki* (Baker).

10b Shell rather loosely coiled (adults 5-7 mm. in diameter have 4-4½ whorls); ribs distinct on base of shell. Fig. 164.................
....*Discus cronkhitei* (Newcomb)

WIDTH: 5-7 mm. RANGE: Maine to Maryland, west to Washington and California.

Shell with 3½-4½ whorls; tan to light brown. Spire depressed. Umbilicus about 1/3 the diameter of the shell.

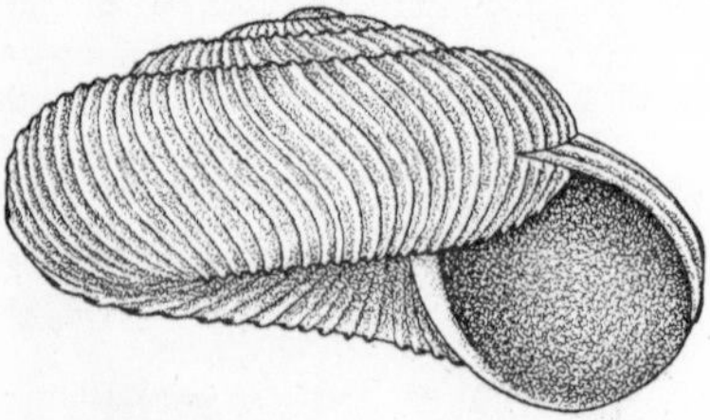

Figure 164. *Discus cronkhitei* (Newcomb.)

11a Periphery of last whorl angular or subangular...............12

11b Periphery of last whorl flattened or concave, singly or doubly carinate 13

12a Shell with darker brown or reddish-brown spots. Fig. 165......
....*Discus rotundatus* (Müller)

WIDTH: 6 mm. RANGE: Introduced into Massachusetts, New York, New Jersey.

Shell with 6 whorls; ground color yellowish-brown. The periphery of the last whorl is sometimes rounded (Fig. 161).

Figure 165. *Discus rotundatus* (Müller).

12b Shell uniform in color; without darker spots. Fig. 166.........
.........................*Discus cronkhitei catskillensis* (Pilsbry)

WIDTH: 5 mm. RANGE: Maine to Pennsylvania, west to Minnesota, South Dakota.

Shell with about 4 whorls; pale brown. Differs from *D. cronkhitei*, s.s., by the angular periphery and wider umbilicus.

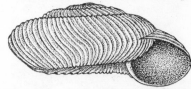

Figure 166. *Discus cronkhitei catskillensis* (Pilsbry).

13a Shell doubly carinate; periphery of last whorl deeply concave. Fig. 167...............................*Discus clappi* (Pilsbry)

WIDTH: 7.4 mm. RANGE: Alabama.

Shell with 5-5½ whorls; very pale tan. Strongly depressed and very widely umbilicate. Lip complete. Similar to *D. bryanti* (Fig. 168), but with more exaggerated characters. Aperture bell-shaped.

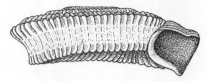

Figure 167. *Discus clappi* (Pilsbry).

13b Shell singly carinate; periphery of last whorl flattened or only slightly concave. Fig. 168................*Discus bryanti* (Harper)

WIDTH: 6.5-7.5 mm. RANGE: Tennessee, North Carolina, Alabama.

Shell with 5-5½ whorls; light brown. Lip complete. Similar to *D. clappi* (Fig. 167), but with less exaggerated characters.

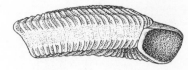

Figure 168. *Discus bryanti* (Harper).

14a Shell surface sculptured with well-developed raised spiral lirae..15

14b Shell surface either smooth or with microscopic striae or puncta 17

15a Spiral lirae unequal in size, some conspicuously fringed. Fig. 169.
...............................*Helicodiscus fimbriatus* **Wetherby**

WIDTH: 5 mm. RANGE: Tennessee, North Carolina, Georgia, Alabama.

Shell with about 5 whorls; light yellowish-green; disk-shaped, the spire hardly raised above the body whorl; very widely umbilicate.

Figure 169. *Helicodiscus fimbriatus* Wetherby.

15b Spiral lirae equal in size, not fringed.........................16

16a Spiral lirae well-developed on all whorls. Fig. 170.............
...............................*Helicodiscus eigenmanni* **Pilsbry**

WIDTH: 3.5-4.8 mm. RANGE: South Dakota, Texas, New Mexico, Arizona.

Shell with 4½-5½ whorls; corneous. Aperture broadly lunate, with several deep-set teeth. Generally larger than *H. parallelus* (Fig. 171).

Figure 170. *Helicodiscus eigenmanni* Pilsbry.

16b Spiral lirae absent or very poorly developed on the first one or two whorls. Fig. 171................*Helicodiscus parallelus* **(Say)**

WIDTH: 3.2-3.5 mm. RANGE: Maine to Alabama, west to South Dakota and Oklahoma.

Shell with 4-4½ whorls; pale yellow with a faint greenish cast; the spire very slightly convex.

Figure 171. *Helicodiscus parallelus* (Say).

17a Shell surface with spiral puncta. Fig. 172.......................
...........................*Helicodiscus punctatellus* **Morrison**

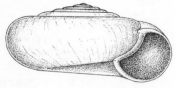

WIDTH: 3.4 mm. RANGE: Kentucky.

Shell with 4½ whorls; white, translucent. Unbilicus wide, about 1/3 the diameter of the shell. Spire slightly raised.

Figure 172. *Helicodiscus punctatellus* Morrison.

17b Shell surface smooth, microscopically striate, or if punctate the puncta are not spirally arranged..............................18

18a Shells with 3½-4 whorls measure 2-3 mm. in diameter. Fig. 173.
............................*Helicodiscus singleyanus* (Pilsbry)

RANGE: New Jersey to Florida, west to South Dakota and California.

Shell with 3½-4½ whorls; corneous, sometimes faintly yellowish; rather widely umbilicate, the umbilicus about 1/3 the diameter of the shell.

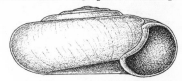

Figure 173. *Helicodiscus singleyanus* (Pilsbry).

18b Shells with 3½-4 whorls are less than 2 mm. in diameter. Fig. 174..............................*Helicodiscus nummus* (Vanatta)

WIDTH: 1.5 mm. RANGE: Indiana, Texas.

Shell with 3½-4 whorls; white, translucent; disc-shaped. Spire greatly depressed, umbilicus wide.

Figure 174. *Helicodiscus nummus* (Vanatta).

19a Shell aperture without teeth or laminae......................20

19b Shell aperture with a basal lamina. Fig. 175.................
....*Punctum smithi* Morrison

WIDTH: 1.1-1.2 mm. RANGE: Virginia, Alabama, Kentucky.

Shell with 4-4½ whorls; very pale tan or brown, with a slight greenish tint; spirally striate. Periphery of whorls oval in outline.

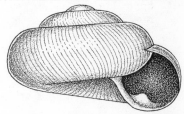

Figure 175. *Punctum smithi* Morrison (after Morrison).

20a Shell with major riblets low and relatively closely spaced (on the body whorl there are usually less than 5 minor riblets between each two major riblets) (Fig. 176, a)........................21

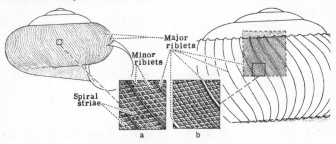

Figure 176

20b Shell with major riblets widely spaced and more prominent (on the body whorl there are usually more than 5 minor riblets between each two major riblets). Fig. 176, b; 177 . . . .
. . . . *Punctum vitreum* Baker

WIDTH: 1.2-1.4 mm. RANGE: New Jersey to Virginia, west to Iowa and Texas.

Shell with 4-4½ whorls; light corneous to colorless and translucent; spirally striate. Umbilicus rather wide.

Figure 177. *Punctum vitreum* Baker
(after Baker).

21a Shell relatively large, 1.5 mm. or more in diameter. Fig. 178 . . . . . .
. . . . *Punctum californicum* Pilsbry

WIDTH: 1.5-1.8 mm. RANGE: South Dakota, Montana, Colorado, Arizona, California.

Shell with 3-4½ whorls; light chestnut; with faint spiral striae. Umbilicus rather narrow and deep.

Figure 178. *Punctum californicum* Pilsbry

21b Shell smaller, 1.3 mm. or less in diameter 22

22a Shell somewhat depressed; last whorl deflected. Fig. 179 . . . .
. . . . *Punctum minutissimum* (Lea)

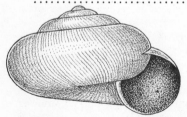

WIDTH: 1.1-1.3 mm. RANGE: Maine to Florida, west to Oregon and New Mexico.

Shell with 3½-4½ whorls; pale brown to corneous; somewhat translucent; with fine, spiral striae.

Figure 179. *Punctum minutissimum* (Lea)

22b Shell more depressed; last whorl not deflected. Fig. 180.........
...................................*Punctum blandianum* Pilsbry

WIDTH: 1.1-1.3 mm. RANGE: Tennessee, Virginia, Alabama.
Shell with about 4 whorls; pale
brown; spirally striate. Umbilicus
wider than in *P. minutissimum* (Fig.
179).

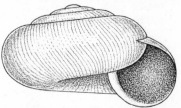

Figure 180. *Punctum blandianum*
Pilsbry

LIMACIDAE

This family of slugs is native to Europe and adjacent parts of
Asia and Africa; some species of one of its genera, *Deroceras*, also
occur naturally in northern Asia and North America. All other members of this family in the Eastern United States have been introduced,
mainly from Europe. They can be distinguished from the philomycids
by the smaller, anterior mantle, and from the arionids by the posterior
position of the breathing pore in the mantle, the keeled back, posteriorly
pointed tail of the foot, and absence of a mucous gland there.

1a Back strongly keeled; mantle granulate but not concentrically
wrinkled, its center part bounded by a groove. Fig. 181.........
...................................*Milax gagates* (Draparnaud)

LENGTH: 60-70 mm.*
RANGE: Introduced
into New York, Penn-
sylvania, Virginia,
Colorado, Washing-
ton, Oregon, Cali-
fornia.

Figure 181. *Milax gagates* (Draparnaud)

Dark gray or black, without darker or lighter bands. Posterior end
pointed, without a mucous pore. This "Greenhouse Slug" is a destructive pest in gardens and greenhouses. It is largely subterranean
in habit, burrowing in the soil and feeding on roots.

1b Back keeled only near the end; mantle concentrically wrinkled,
without a groove...2

2a Animal large, 50 mm. or more when extended; body usually either
banded or conspicuously spotted..............................3

2b Animal medium or small, 50 mm. or less in length when extended;
body not banded, and if spotted, either inconspicuously spotted or
mottled. Genus *Deroceras*....................................5

*Measurements given for members of this family refer to the animal rather than
to the internal shell.

3a Mantle and back with dark longitudinal bands; body color generally light brown or yellowish-gray; mucus colorless. Fig. 182....
......................................*Lehmannia poirieri* (Mabille)
LENGTH: 50-60 mm. RANGE: Introduced into New York, Missouri, Colorado(?), Arizona, California.
Both the pedal and suprapedal grooves are prominent. The mantle is concentrically wrinkled.

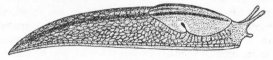

Figure 182. *Lehmannia poirieri* (Mabille)

3b Mantle and usually back spotted or mottled rather than with continuous bands; body color yellowish to gray; mucus yellow or colorless. Genus *Limax*..4

4a Mantle and body black-spotted; mucus colorless. Fig. 183........
....*Limax maximus* Linné
LENGTH: 80-120 mm. RANGE: Introduced and spread from Massachusetts to Virginia, west to Oregon and California.
This slug is common in urban and suburban gardens, cellars, and similar places.

Figure 183. *Limax maximus* Linné

4b Mantle and body gray with yellowish spots; mucus yellow. Fig. 184...*Limax flavus* Linné
LENGTH: 75-100 mm. RANGE: Introduced into eastern states from Maine to Alabama; Indiana, Illinois, Missouri, Arkansas, Texas, Arizona, California.
The habits of *L. flavus* in this country are very similar to those of *Deroceras reticulatum* (Fig. 185). It is a slug of urban and suburban gardens, greenhouses, and other cultivated places.

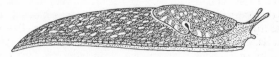

Fig. 184. *Limax flavus* Linné.

5a Animal medium in size, 35-50 mm. when extended; whitish, cream or flesh-colored with gray markings; mantle situated forward near the head; exudes milky adhesive slime when irritated. Fig. 185.
...................................*Deroceras reticulatum* (Müller)
LENGTH: 35-50 mm. RANGE: Introduced and spread throughout the United States generally, except for south Atlantic and Gulf states.
Commonly known as the "Gray Garden Slug," this species has been introduced by commerce into nearly every temperate and subtropical country settled by Europeans. It is gregarious and in countries where it is introduced is usually confined to the vicinity of towns and cultivated areas. It is a destructive pest in gardens, feeding on almost any vegetable crop, and is especially injurious to young plants.

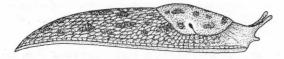

Figure 185. *Deroceras reticulatum* (Müller)

5b Animal small, about 25 mm. when extended; usually uniformly yellowish, sometimes flecked with gray; mantle situated nearly in middle of body; exudes watery slime when irritated. Fig. 186.
....*Deroceras laeve* (Müller)
LENGTH: 15-30 mm. RANGE: Introduced and spread throughout the United Statest generally.
This species is smaller and more uniform in color than *D. reticulatum.*

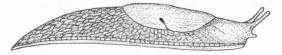

Figure 186. *Deroceras laeve* (Müller)

ZONITIDAE

This family of medium to small snails is almost world-wide in its distribution. The shell is usually perforate or umbilicate, and generally has a depressed spire. The lip is thin and not reflected. The animal has the margin of the foot defined by a pedal groove, like other aulacopod snails. Members of the genus *Oxychilus*, usually found in gardens and in and around greenhouses and cellars, have been introduced from Europe.

1a Shell with few (3 or less) rapidly enlarging whorls, usually imperforate, very thin. The aperture is unusually large, larger than the rest of the shell when seen in side view (Fig. 187, a)............2

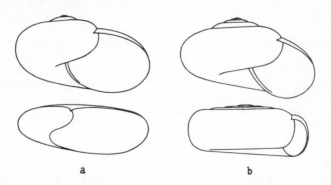

a   b

Fig. 187. a) Shells with very wide body whorls and apertures. b) Shells with narrower body whorls and apertures.

1b Shell with 3 or more whorls which increase slowly in size; thicker. The aperture is smaller than the rest of the shell when seen in side view (Fig. 187, b)...4

2a Shell small, diameter 6 mm. or less; colorless or with a pale greenish tint. Subfamily Vitrininae. Fig. 188..........................
....*Vitrina limpida* Gould

WIDTH: 6 mm. RANGE: Maine, Massachusetts, New York, Pennsylvania and Michigan.
Shell with 2-3 rapidly increasing whorls, glossy and transparent, very thin and fragile. The first whorl has microscopic spiral pits.

Fig. 188. *Vitrina limpida* Gould.

2b Shell large, diameter 16 mm. or more; dark olive-green or dresdenbrown. Subfamily Zonitinae (in part). Genus *Vitrinizonites*......3

84

**3a Shell extremely thin and fragile, almost completely devoid of cal-
careous material. Fig. 189.........*Vitrinizonites uvidermis* Pilsbry**

WIDTH: 17-19 mm. RANGE: North
Carolina and Tennessee.

Shell with 2½-3 whorls; dresdenbrown to blackish. The shell of this
species is very similar to that of
V. latissimus (Fig. 190), but usually

Fig. 189. *Vitrinizonites uvidermis*
Pilsbry.

dented and distorted, even on living
snails. The shell surface is also usually less brilliant than that of *V.
latissimus.*

**3b Shell thicker, with enough calcium carbonate to prevent wrinkles
or distortions of its shape. Fig. 190..*Vitrinizonites latissimus* (Lewis)**

WIDTH: 16.2-19.5 mm. RANGE: North
Carolina, Tennessee and Alabama.

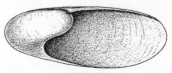

Shell with 2½-3 whorls; dresdenbrown to olive, yellow or green,
glossy. The spire is small and flat,
slightly sunken. The upper shell sur-

Fig. 190. *Vitrinizonites latissimus*
(Lewis).

face is marked with conspicious, unevenly spaced, radial grooves which
fade out at the shell periphery.

**4a Shell rather widely to very widely umbilicate; aperture and/or body
whorl containing teeth..5**

**4b Shell usually perforate to narrowly umbilicate; aperture and body
whorl with or without teeth (those few species having a wide umbilicus lack teeth in the aperture and body whorl)..............8**

**5a Shell aperture with a parietal tooth in addition to other teeth. Fig.
191....................................*Pilsbryna tridens* Morrison**

WIDTH: 1.6 mm. RANGE: Oklahoma
and Texas.

Shell with 4 whorls; whitish to corneous; growth lines not prominent, irregularly spaced. The aperture is roundly-
lunate and greatly constricted by the
three teeth. The lip is sharp and simple.

Fig. 191. *Pilsbryna tridens*
Morrison, after Morrison).

5b Shell aperture without a parietal tooth........................6

6a Shell minute, 1.5 mm. in diameter; 4 whorls; aperture as wide as high. Fig. 192.......................*Paravitrea roundyi* Morrison

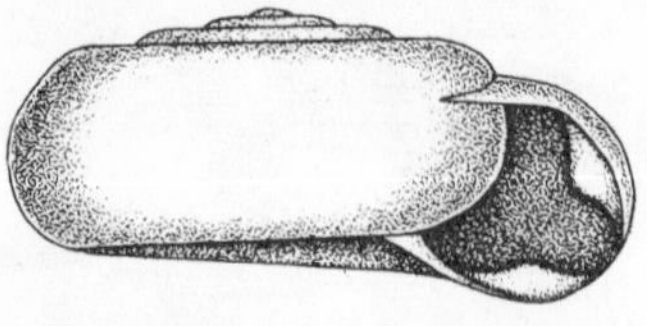

RANGE: Oklahoma.

Shell with 4 whorls; whitish; smooth. The whorls are rather sharply shouldered. This species is very similar to *Hawaiia minuscula* (see Fig. 254), but may be distinguished by the teeth in the aperture.

Fig. 192. *Paravitrea roundyi* Morrison (after Morrison).

6b Shell larger, 2-3.5 mm. in diameter; 5 whorls; aperture narrow or deeply crescentic. Genus *Clappiella*...........................7

7a Shell disk-shaped, spire almost flat; sculptured with regular spiral rows of beads or papillae. Fig. 193..*Clappiella saludensis* (Morrison)

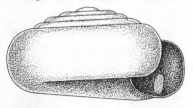

WIDTH: 2.4-3.5 mm. RANGE: South Carolina.

Shell with 4½-5½ whorls; pale green. The external appearance of the shell of this species is superficially very similar to *Helicodiscus parallelus* (see Fig. 171), but dif-

Figure 193. *Clappiella saludensis* (Morrison)

fers from that species in being sculptured with spiral rows of beads rather than ridges. The arrangement of the teeth are different in the two species.

7b Shell depressed, almost disk-shaped, spire slightly raised above the body whorl; without sculpture of spiral rows of beads or papillae. Fig. 194...........................*Clappiella aldrichiana* (Clapp)

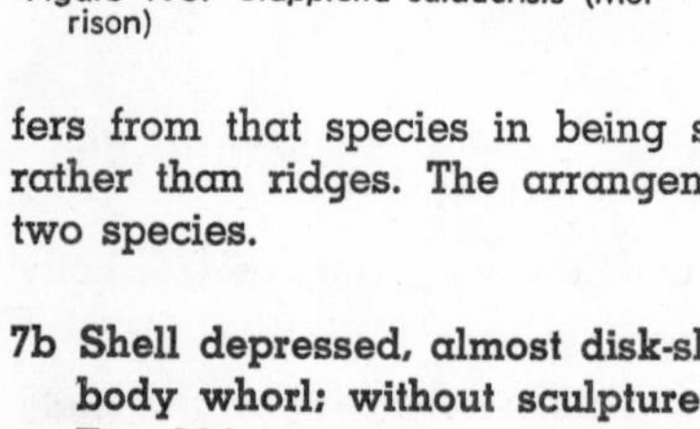

WIDTH: 2-2.9 mm. RANGE: Tennessee and Alabama.

Shell with 5 whorls; greenish-white, semi-transparent, glossy; sculptured with faint growth lines. There are usually four teeth just below the periphery in the last half of the body whorl. Alternating with these are smaller teeth on the columellar side.

Fig. 194. *Clappiella alarichiana* (Clapp) (after Clapp).

8a Shell scultpured with ribs or riblets............................9

8b Shell without ribs or riblets....................................13

9a Shell relatively large, more than 6 mm. in diameter; upper surface sculptured with ribs, base smooth; spiral striae absent. Fig. 195.
....*Gastrodonta interna* (Say)

WIDTH: 6.5-7.4 mm. RANGE: North Carolina and Georgia, west to Indiana and Tennessee.

Shell with 8-9 whorls; cinnamon-brown to buff. The first several whorls are microscopically granulated. The aperture contains two teeth which are situated on a callous ridge. Young shells have two or three rows of such teeth.

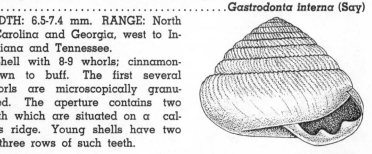

Fig. 195. *Gastrodonta interna* (Say).

9b Shell small (less than 3.5 mm. in diameter), often minute; upper and lower surfaces sculptured with riblets and fine spiral striae. Genus *Striatura*...10

10a Shell relatively large, 2.5 mm. or more in diameter; umbilicus relatively narrow, 1/5 or less the diameter of the shell; riblets not distinct. Fig. 196..........................*Striatura ferrea* Morse

WIDTH: 2.5-3.4 mm. RANGE: Maine to North Carolina, west to Michigan and Tennessee.

Shell with 3½-4 whorls; grayish, translucent, rather dull. The rapid increase in whorl

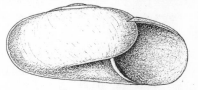

Fig. 196. *Striatura ferrea* Morse.

size in this species is very similar to that characteristic of *Retinella* (p. 95 ff.). The animal is colored dark blue or black.

10b Shell smaller, less than 2.5 mm. in diameter; umbilicus wider, ¼ or more the diameter of the shell; riblets distinct..............11

11a Shell more than 2 mm. in diameter; riblets high and widely spaced (30-40 on last whorl). Fig. 197.........*Striatura exigua* (Stimpson)

WIDTH: 2.2-2.4 mm. RANGE: Maine to Pennsylvania, west to Ohio, Michigan and Minnesota.

Shell with about 3½ whorls; corneous with a greenish cast. The radial (transverse) riblets are more oblique than growth lines and are more widely spaced than in other species of the genus.

Fig. 197. *Striatura exigua* (Stimpson).

11b Shell less than 2 mm. in diameter; riblets low and closely spaced (many more than 40 on last whorl)..........................12

12a Shell 1.7-1.8 mm. in diameter; spiral striae prominent. Fig. 198...
......................*Striatura meridionalis* (Pilsbry and Ferriss)

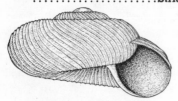

Fig. 198. *Striatura meridionalis* (Pilsbry and Ferriss).

WIDTH: 1.7-1.8 mm. RANGE: New Jersey to Florida, west to Missouri and Arizona.

Shell with 3-3½ whorls; corneous with a greenish cast. It is similar to *S. milium* (Fig. 199), but is larger and has coarser riblets. Like most other members of the genus it prefers low, wet ground.

12b Shell smaller, about 1.5 mm. in diameter; spiral striae not prominent. Fig. 199..........................*Striatura milium* (Morse)

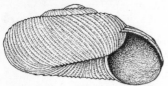

Fig. 199. *Striatura milium* (Morse).

RANGE: Maine to Pennsylvania and West Virginia, west to Michigan and Kentucky.

Shell with 3-3½ whorls; corneous-yellow to gray. The animal is white, with dark spots on its head and tentacles. This species is one of the smallest land snails in the United States.

13a Whorls increasing regularly in size, the last very much wider (Fig. 200, a); without teeth in aperture or body whorl. Subfamily Zonitinae (in part)..14

13b Whorls narrow, tightly coiled, increasing very slowly in size (Fig. 200, b); with or without teeth in aperture and/or body whorl. Subfamilies Zonitinae (in part), Gastrodontinae, Euconulinae.......54

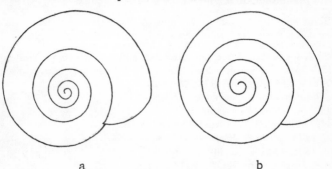

a   b

Fig. 200. Shell with a) regularly increasing whorls, b) slowly increasing whorls.

14a Shell large, 16 mm. or more in diameter. Genus *Mesomphix*...15
14b Shell smaller, usually 15 mm. or less in diameter..............26
15a Shell perforate, or very narrowly umbilicate, umbilicus less than
    1/12 the shell diameter.....................................16
15b Shell umbilicus wider, 1/12 to 1/5 the shell diameter..........22
16a First several whorls of spire nearly smooth...................17
16b First several whorls of spire strongly sculptured with growth
    wrinkles 18
17a Last whorl rapidly enlarging, making the aperture relatively large
    and the spire relatively small; spire diameter ½ or less shell
    diameter. Fig. 201...............*Mesomphix andrewsae* (Pilsbry)

WIDTH: 16.3-21 mm. RANGE: Virginia,
North Carolina and Tennessee.

Shell with 4½-5 whorls; olive to dark
chestnut brown, glossy; sculptured with
weak, low, inconspicuous growth wrinkles. Minute, spirally arranged papillae may be seen under high magnification.

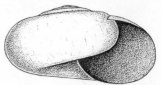

Fig. 201. *Mesomphix andrewsae*
(Pilsbry).

17b Last whorl smaller, with smaller aperture; spire relatively larger,
    its diameter more than ½ the shell diameter. Fig. 202........
    ....*Mesomphix inornatus* (Say)

WIDTH: 16.6-21 mm. RANGE: Vermont to Virginia, west to Indiana
and Kentucky.

Shell with 5 whorls; olive-tan. The
shell of this species is very similar
to *M. andrewsae* (Fig. 201), but the
umbilical perforation is slightly larger and the surface more glossy. The

Fig. 202. *Mesomphix inornatus*
(Say).

most conspicuous difference is in the wider spire.

18a. Shell height more than ½ its diameter........................19
18b. Shell height ½ or less of its diameter........................21
19a Aperture height and width about equal. Fig. 203..............
    ....*Mesomphix rugeli* (Binney)

WIDTH: 16-22.5 mm. RANGE: Virginia,
North Carolina and Tennessee.

Shell with 5½-6 whorls; greenish-horn.
This species is somewhat similar to *M.
subplanus* (Fig. 207), but is less depressed and the last whorl is much
larger. The shell sculpture usually does
not include spiral striae.

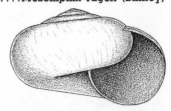

Fig. 203. *Mesomphix rugeli*
(Binney).

19b Aperture width distinctly greater than height.................**20**

**20a Shell rather dull; sculpture of fine spiral papillae well developed.
Fig. 204**...........................*Mesomphix vulgatus* **Baker**

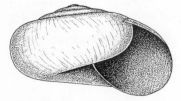

Fig. 204. *Mesomphix vulgatus* Baker.

WIDTH: 16-27.8 mm. RANGE: Pennsylvania to Florida, west to Illinois and Louisiana.

Shell with 4½-5½ whorls; olive-tan with darker and lighter streaks. The shell surface is fine and evenly sculptured with growth wrinkles. They fade out at the glossy base of the shell.

20b Shell more glossy; sculpture of fine spiral papillae not well developed. Fig. 205..................*Mesomphix perlaevis* **(Pilsbry)**

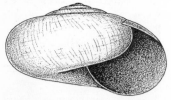

Fig. 205. *Mesomphix perlaevis* (Pilsbry).

WIDTH: 17.6-20.7 mm. RANGE: North Carolina, Kentucky and Tennessee. Shell with 4½-5 whorls; light olive. The shell is rather thin, depressed, and minutely umbilicate. The base is somewhat smoother than the upper surface, and is strongly convex.

21a Last whorl rapidly enlarging, making the spire relatively small, hardly more than ½ the shell diameter; sculptured with rows of microscopic spiral papillae. Fig. 206....*Mesomphix latior* **(Pilsbry)**

Fig. 206. *Mesomphix latior* (Pilsbry).

WIDTH: 20.5-28 mm. RANGE: North Carolina, Georgia, Tennessee and Alabama.

Shell with 4½-5 whorls; olive-tan with darker and lighter streaks. The shell of this species is very similar to that of *M. vulgatus* (Fig. 204) and *M. perlaevis* (Fig. 205), but it is more depressed and has a broader body whorl.

21b Last whorl smaller, making the spire relatively large, distinctly more than ½ the shell diameter; surface without spiral rows of fine papillae. Fig. 207............*Mesomphix subplanus* (Binney)

WIDTH: 16.3-23 mm. RANGE: North Carolina and Tennessee.

Shell with 5½-6 whorls; brownish or smoky horn-colored, glossy. The first several whorls are sharply marked with growth wrinkles. The umbilical opening is very small, usually less than 1 mm. in diameter.

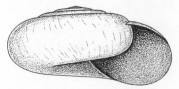

Fig. 207. *Mesomphix subplanus* (Binney).

22a Shell relatively small, 16.5 mm. or less in diameter; strongly depressed, spire hardly visible above the body whorl. Fig. 208.... ....*Oxychilus draparnaldi* (Beck)

WIDTH: 12-16.5 mm. RANGE: Introduced into many Atlantic states (Massachusetts to South Carolina); also into Illinois, Colorado, Washington, Oregon and California.

Shell with 5-5½ whorls; highly polished, semi-transparent; amber or pale yellowish. The whorls are well-rounded at the periphery and are sculptured with fine, irregular growth lines. The sutures are moderately impressed.

Fig. 208. *Oxychilus draparnaldi* (Beck).

22b Shell large, more than 16.5 mm. in diameter; less strongly depressed 23

23a Shell sculptured with distinct spiral rows of papillae..........24

23b. Shell sculpture indistinct....................................25

24a Shell larger, more than 29 mm. in diameter; spiral papillae not very well developed. Fig. 209......*Mesomphix capnodes* (Binney)

WIDTH: 29.5-35.5 mm. RANGE: Georgia, Tennessee and Alabama.

Shell with 5 whorls; horn-colored. The relative height of the shell varies greatly. The umbilicus is about 1/10-1/8 the shell diameter, rarely larger.

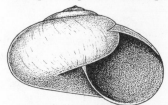

Fig. 209. *Mesomphix capnodes* (Binney).

24b Shell smaller, 27 mm. or less in diameter; spiral papillae well developed. Fig. 210..................Mesomphix pilsbryi (Clapp)

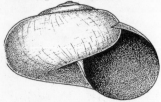

Fig. 210. *Mesomphix pilsbryi* (Clapp).

WIDTH: 16.8-27 mm. RANGE: South Carolina and Alabama.

Shell with 5-5½ whorls; dark reddish-brown. The upper surface of the shell is rather dull, the base glossy. The apex is smooth, and usually has its epidermis worn off.

25a Umbilicus 1/6-1/5 the shell diameter. Fig. 211.................. ....Mesomphix cupreus (Rafinesque)

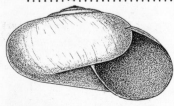

Fig. 211. *Mesomphix cupreus* (Rafinesque).

WIDTH: 22-28.4 mm. RANGE: Vermont to Georgia, west to Michigan and Arkansas.

Shell with 4½-5 whorls; brownish-olive to yellow. The shell of this species is very similar to *M. capnodes* (Fig. 209), but is smaller, has less distinct sculpture and the umbilicus is usually wider. The epidermis of the apex is usually worn off.

25b Umbilicus about 1/10 the shell diameter. Fig. 212.............. ....Mesomphix friabilis (Binney)

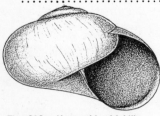

Fig. 212. *Mesomphix friabilis* (Binney).

WIDTH: 21-26.3 mm. RANGE: Indiana to Alabama, west to Kansas and Texas.

Shell with 4½-5 whorls; light brownish-olive, moderately glossy. The shell of this species is very similar to *M. cupreus* (Fig. 211), but differs by its more closely coiled early whorls, smaller apex, and unworn apical whorls.

26a Shell 6 mm. or more in diameter; without radiating indented lines. Genus Oxychilus...27

Fig. 213. Shell with indented radiating lines.

26b Shell, usually less than 6 mm. in diameter, or if larger, with radiating indented lines (Fig. 213). Genera *Retinella, Paravitrea* (in part), *Pilsbryna* (in part)........................29

27a Shell 6-7 mm. in diameter; animal very dark. Fig. 214. . . . .
. . . . *Oxychilus alliarius* (Miller)

RANGE: Introduced into New York,
New Jersey, Colorado and California.

Shell with 4-4½ whorls; highly polished; amber or pale yellowish. In
living specimens the shell color is
difficult to discern because the thin,
semi-transparent nature of the shell

Fig. 214. *Oxychilus alliarius* (Miller).

allows the dark body of the animal to show through. The spire is
hardly raised above the body whorl, giving the shell a discoidal
appearance.

**27b Shell 9 mm. or more in diameter; animal either very pale or very
dark** **28**

28a Shell about 9 mm. in diameter; animal pale gray. Fig. 215. . . . . .
. . . . *Oxychilus cellarius* (Müller)

RANGE: Introduced into many Atlantic states (Maine to South Carolina); also into Michigan, Indiana,
Illinois, Missouri, Oregon and California.

Shell with 5 whorls. This species
is intermediate in size between O.

Fig. 215. *Oxychilus cellarius* (Müller).

alliarius (Fig. 214) and *O. draparnaldi*
(Fig. 216). It is most easily distinguished from those two species by
the light color of the animal and the more broadly lunate shell aperture.

**28b Shell 12-16.5 mm. in diameter; animal dark blue-black or blue-
gray. Fig. 216.** . . . .*Oxychilus draparnaldi* (Beck)

RANGE: Introduced into many Atlantic states (Massachusetts to
South Carolina); also into Illinois, Colorado, Washington, Oregon and California.

Shell with 5-5½ whorls; highly
polished, semi-transparent; amber
or pale yellowish. The whorls are

Fig. 216. *Oxychilus draparnaldi* (Beck).

well-rounded at the periphery and are sculptured with fine, irregular
growth lines. The sutures are moderately impressed.

**29a Shell with radiating indented lines in addition to its ordinary
growth lines or wrinkles** **30**

**29b Shell without radiating indented lines in addition to its ordinary
growth lines or wrinkles** **52**

Fig. 217. *Paravitrea petrophila* (Bland).

WIDTH: 5.7-6 mm. RANGE: Kentucky, Tennessee and Arkansas.

Shell with 5½-6 whorls; whitish, glossy, translucent and thin. The aperture is ovate-lunate, the peristome simple. The columellar margin is slightly reflected.

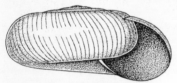

Fig. 218. *Paravitrea aulacogyra* (Pilsbry and Ferriss) (after Pilsbry and Ferriss).

RANGE: Arkansas.

Shell with 5½-6 whorls; whitish. The shell of this species is very similar to *P. petrophila* (Fig. 217) except for its larger size, relatively smaller umbilicus and different surface sculpture.

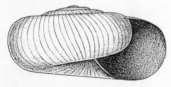

Fig. 219. *Pilsbryna castanea* Baker.

WIDTH: 3.6-3.7 mm. RANGE: Tennessee.

Shell with about 5½ whorls; yellowish. This species is similar to *P. aurea* (see Fig. 257), but has a larger umbilicus and the lamellae of the body whorl (usually not present in adults) have a different arrangement.

34b Shell 4.5 mm. or more in diameter.........................**35**

35a Umbilicus wider, more than ¼ the shell diameter. Fig. 220.....
.................................*Retinella pentadelphia* (Pilsbry)

WIDTH: 5 mm. RANGE: North Carolina, Georgia and Tennessee.

Shell with about 4½ whorls; pinkish-brown, glossy. The shell is strongly depressed, rather widely umbilicate, with an ovate-lunate aperture. The lip is sharp and simple, the columellar margin slightly reflected.

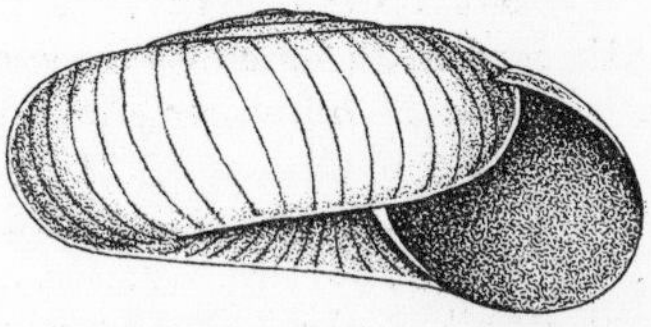

Fig. 220. *Retinella pentadelphia* (Pilsbry).

35b Umbilicus narrower, less than 1/5 the shell diameter. Fig. 221...
.................................*Retinella rhoadsi* (Pilsbry)

WIDTH: 4.5-5.3 mm. RANGE: Maine to North Carolina, west to Michigan and Tennessee.

Shell with 4-5 whorls; corneous. The radiating indented lines of this species are somewhat similar to those of *R. indentata* (see Fig. 239), but the shells differ in the width of the umbilicus.

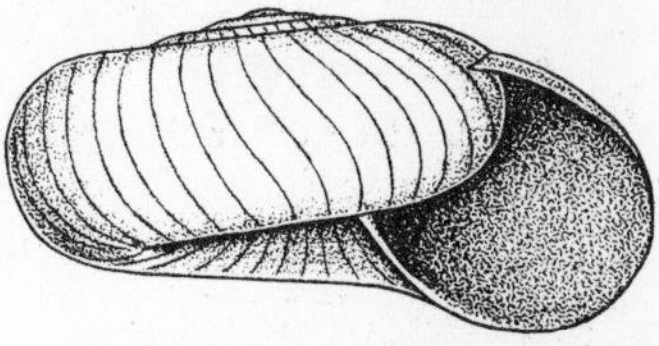

Fig. 221. *Retinella rhoadsi* (Pilsbry).

36a Shell light horn to buff-colored; radiating indented lines widely and irregularly spaced......................................**37**

36b Shell whitish; radiating indented lines closely and regularly spaced **45**

37a Umbilicus nearly circular in outline. Fig. 222, a.............**38**

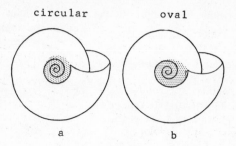

circular   oval

a   b

Fig. 222. a) Umbilicus circular in outline. b) Umbilicus oval in outline.

38a Shell with raised spire. Fig. 223...*Retinella circumstriata* (Taylor)

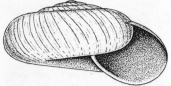

WIDTH: 4.6 mm. RANGE: Alabama.

Shell with 4-4½ whorls; pale yellow, sculptured with very close, microscopic, spiral striae. Shell narrowly umbilicate, the umbilicus about
1/6 the shell diameter.

Fig. 223. *Retinella circumstriata*
(Taylor).

38b Shell strongly depressed.....................................39

39a Shell more than 4 mm. in diameter. Fig. 224...................
.................................*Retinella virginica* Morrison

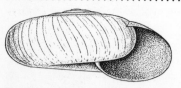

WIDTH: 4.1-5.3 mm. RANGE: Virginia.

Shell with 5-5½ whorls; pinkish-
horn, sculptured with minute spiral
striae. The umbilicus is funicular, its
diameter 1/4-1/3 the shell diameter.
The aperture is triangularly- to ovate-
lunate.

Fig. 224. *Retinella virginica* Morrison.

39b Shell 4 mm. or less in diameter...........................40

40a Shell 3.9-4 mm. in diameter. Fig. 225...................................
.................................*Retinella burringtoni* (Pilsbry)

RANGE: New York and Connecticut,
south to Virginia and West Virginia.

Shell with about 4½ whorls; buff,
glossy, semi-translucent. The shell of
this species resembles *R. rhoadsi* (see
Fig. 221), but the radial grooves are
not as widely spaced and the growth

Fig. 225. *Retinella burringtoni* (Pilsbry).

lines are more strongly developed. The minute spiral striae are more
distinct than in *R. virginica* (Fig. 224).

40b Shell 3 mm. or less in diameter. Fig. 226.....................
...............................*Retinella cumberlandiana* (Clapp)

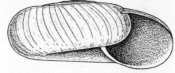

WIDTH: 2.7-3 mm. RANGE: North
Carolina, Tennessee and Alabama.

Shell with 4-4½ whorls; light horn-
colored, glossy, semi-transparent. The
umbilicus is about ¼ the shell diameter. The shell of this species is very

Fig. 226. *Retinella cumberlandiana* (Clapp).

similar to *R. burringtoni* (Fig. 225), but is smaller.

41a Umbilicus wide, 1/5 or 1/6 the shell diameter; shell color yel-
lowish, reddish or brownish...................................42

41b Umbilicus narrower, less than 1/8 the shell diameter; shell color
greenish-horn. Fig. 227..*Retinella approxima* (Walker and Pilsbry)

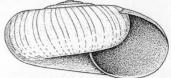

WIDTH: 4.5 mm. RANGE: North Carolina.

Shell with about 4½ whorls; greenish-horn, glossy. The shell of this
species is very similar to that of *R.
vanattai* (see Fig. 229), but differs in
color, in having a less depressed body

Fig. 227. *Retinella approxima* (Walker and Pilsbry).

whorl, more crowded and shallower radial grooves, which are less distinct beneath, and in its narrower umbilicus.

42a Shell 3.6-3.7 mm. in diameter. Fig. 228...*Pilsbryna castanea* Baker
RANGE: Tennessee.

Fig. 228. *Pilsbryna castanea* Baker.

Shell with about 5½ whorls; yellowish. This species is simliar to *P. aurea* (see Fig. 257), but has a larger umbilicus and the lamellae of the body whorl (usually not present in adults) have a different arrangement.

42b Shell more than 4 mm. in diameter......................43
43a Shell about 4.5 mm. in diameter. Fig. 229.....................
.......................*Retinella vanattai* (Pilsbry and Walker)

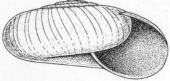

Fig. 229. *Retinella vanattai* (Pilsbry and Walker).

RANGE: North Carolina and Tennessee.

Shell with 5 whorls; yellow, translucent. The irregularly spaced radial grooves are rather deeply impressed on the upper surface of the shell. Additional sculpture consists of growth lines and fine, rather faint, close spiral striae.

43b Shell 5 mm. or more in diameter...........................44
44a Shell 5-5.5 mm. in diameter; color brownish-horn. Fig. 230.....
.....................................*Retinella wheatleyi* (Bland)

Fig. 230. *Retinella wheatleyi* (Bland).

RANGE: New York to Alabama, west to Michigan and Arkansas.

Shell with 5-5½ whorls; brownish to horn-colored, glossy. The sculpture of this species is much like that of *R. circumstriata* (see Fig. 223). Its shape is somewhat like *R. virginica* (see Fig. 224), but the last whorl is more rapidly expanded.

44b Shell about 6.5 mm. in diameter; yellowish to reddish. Fig. 231.
.....................................*Retinella clingmani* (Dall)

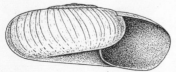

Fig. 231. *Retinella clingmani* (Dall).

RANGE: North Carolina.

Shell with about 5½ whorls; greenish-yellow to reddish-horn, glossy. The shell of this species is very similar to *R. vanattai* (see Fig. 229), but is larger, is differently colored, and the shape of the aperture differs.

45a Umbilicus ¼ the shell diameter; umbilicus walls steeply rounded
....46

45b Umbilicus 1/3 the shell diameter; umbilicus walls flattened and slanting. Fig. 232........................*Retinella raderi* (Dall)

WIDTH: 3.9-4 mm. RANGE: Maryland.

Shell with about 4½ whorls; whitish; very depressed, the spire hardly noticeable above the body whorl. Aperture broadly ovate-lunate.

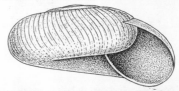

Fig. 232. *Retinella raderi* (Dall) (after Dall).

46a Shell about 3.5 mm. in diameter. Fig. 233...................
..................................*Retinella lewisiana* (Clapp)

RANGE: Tennessee and Alabama.

Shell with 3½-4 whorls; yellowish-white, translucent, very glossy. The shell is sculptured with very minute spiral striae in addition to the transverse lines and grooves.

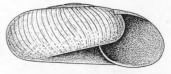

Fig. 233. *Retinella lewisiana* (Clapp).

46b Shell larger, 4 mm. or more in diameter...................47
47a Spire and body whorl relatively high. Fig. 234...............
..................................*Retinella floridana* (Morrison)

WIDTH: 4-4.5 mm. RANGE: Florida.

Shell with 5-5½ whorls; white. The shell of this species is very similar to that of *R. roemeri* (Fig. 235), but its base is more deeply rounded near the umbilicus. Aperture roundly to ovate-lunate.

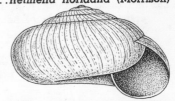

Fig. 234. *Retinella floridana* (Morrison).

47b Spire and body whorl depressed and low. Fig. 235.............
..........................*Retinella roemeri* (Pilsbry and Ferriss)

WIDTH: 4 mm. RANGE: Texas.

Shell with 4½-5 whorls; corneous-white. The shell of this species is very similar to those of *R. wheatleyi* (see Fig. 230) and *Paravitrea petrophila* (see Fig. 217), but the umbilicus is larger, and the transverse sculpture is closer and more regular. It is larger than *R. dalliana* (see Fig. 242).

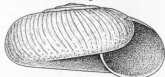

Fig. 235. *Retinella roemeri* (Pilsbry and Ferriss).

48a Shell imperforate. Fig. 236.......*Retinella cryptomphala* (Clapp)

Fig. 236. *Retinella cryptomphala* (Clapp).

WIDTH: 5-7.5 mm. RANGE: Georgia, Kentucky, Tennessee, Alabama and Arkansas(?).

Shell with 5-5½ whorls; light horn to white, translucent, glossy. Shell sculpture consisting of rather evenly-spaced, radiating indented lines, which continue to the base. There are 23-34 of these indented lines on the body whorl. Fine spiral striae are also present.

48b Shell perforate **49**

49a Radiating indented lines closely spaced, about 0.5 mm. apart at periphery of body whorl. Fig. 237.....*Retinella sculptilis* (Bland)

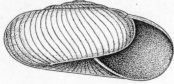

Fig. 237. *Retinella sculptilis* (Bland).

WIDTH: 6.5-12.7 mm. RANGE: North Carolina, Georgia, Tennessee and Alabama.

Shell with 7 whorls; pale horn-colored, glossy. The minute, perforate umbilicus is usually partly covered by an expansion of the columellar lip. This condition is also found in *R. carolinensis*, *R. indentata* and *R. praecox*.

49b Radiating indented lines more widely spaced about 0.7-1.0 mm. apart at periphery of body whorl...........................**50**

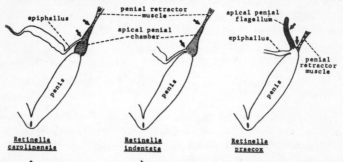

Fig. 238. Male terminal genitalia of a) *Retinella carolinensis*, b) *R indentata*, and c) *R. praecox*. (After Baker.) Arrows indicate key characters.

The characters used in this key to separate the three species to follow, *Retinella carolinensis*, *R. indentata*, and *R. praecox*, are those of the internal soft anatomy. On account of their greatly similar shells they are very difficult to separate using shell characters.

50a Penial retractor muscle terminal. Fig. 238, a, b..............**51**

50b An apical penial flagellum extends past the insertion of the penial retractor muscle. Fig. 238, c..............*Retinella praecox* Baker
WIDTH: 6.2-6.3 mm. RANGE: North Carolina to Georgia, west to Kentucky and Alabama.

Shell with 4½-5 whorls; bronze-colored, translucent. The shell of this species is very similar to *R. indentata* (Fig. 239), but is more depressed, the apical whorls are more tightly coiled, and the last whorl is less capacious.

51a The epiphallus opens near the base of the apical penial chamber. Figs. 238, b; 239......................*Retinella indentata* (Say)

WIDTH: 4.7-7.1 mm. RANGE: Maine to Alabama, west to Utah and Arizona.

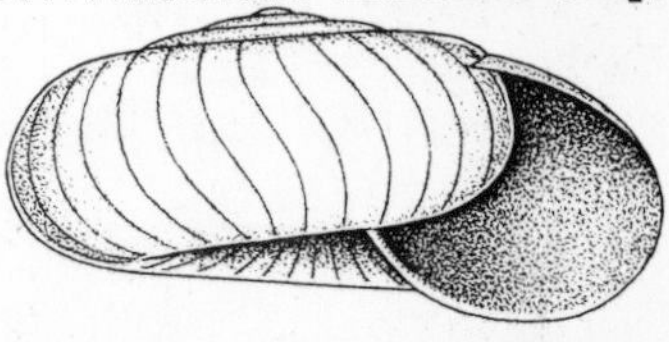

Fig. 239. *Retinella indentata* (Say).

Shell with 4½-5 whorls; corneous, very glossy. The indented radiating lines are widely and nearly equally spaced. There are about 28 of these lines on the body whorl. The shell is also sculptured with faint growth lines and spiral striae.

51b The epiphallus opens near the middle of the apical penial chamber. Fig. 238, a......................*Retinella carolinensis* (Cockerell)
WIDTH: 5-12 mm. RANGE: Virginia, North Carolina and Tennessee.

Shell with 4½-5½ whorls; corneous, glossy, semi-transparent. The shell of this species is very similar to *R. indentata* (Fig. 239), but has more depressed whorls and more conspicuous sculpturing.

52a Shell 4.6-5.2 mm. in diameter. Fig. 240.........................
......................................*Retinella electrina* (Gould)

RANGE: Vermont to Virginia, west to Washington and Arizona.

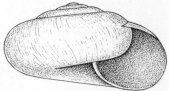

Fig. 240. *Retinella electrina* (Gould)

Shell with 3½-4½ whorls; faint yellow or pale greenish, glossy. The shell of this species is very similar to *R. circumstriata* (see Fig. 223) and *R. burringtoni* (see Fig. 225), but lacks spiral striae. It is also similar to *R. vanattai* (see Fig. 229) and *R. approxima* (see Fig. 227), but has closer transverse sculpture.

52b Shell 4.3 mm. or less in diameter...........................**53**

53a Shell 3.5-4.3 mm. in diameter; nearly colorless. Fig. 241 . . . .
. . . . *. . . . . Retinella binneyana* (Morse)

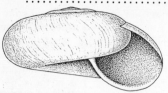

RANGE: Maine to Pennsylvania, west
to Washington and California.

Shell with 3½-4 whorls; nearly colorless, with a greenish tinge. The shell
of this species is very similar to that
of *R. electrina* (Fig. 240), but is smaller
and has a different color.

Fig. 241. *Retinella binneyana* (Morse).

53b Shell 2.6-3.2 mm. in diameter; pale straw-colored. Fig. 242 . . . . .
. . . . *Retinella dalliana* (Pilsbry and Simpson)

RANGE: Florida.

Shell with 3½-4½ whorls; pale straw-
colored, rather glossy. It is marked
with close, irregularly spaced radial
lines and minute spiral striae. The shell
of this species is somewhat similar to
R. lewisiana (see Fig. 233).

Fig. 242. *Retinella dalliana* (Pilsbry
and Simpson).

54a Shell small, less than 4 mm. in diameter **55**
54b Shell larger, more than 4 mm. in diameter **70**
**55a Shell with conspicuously raised spire, often dome-shaped. Sub-
family Euconulinae** **56**
55b Shell depressed, usually strongly so **60**
**56a Shell high-spired, usually dome-shaped; surface with close, fine,
regularly spaced transverse lines. Genus *Euconulus*** **57**
**56b Shell with lower spire, moderately depressed; surface without
close, fine, regularly spaced transverse lines. Genus *Guppya*** . .**58**
57a Shell with 4½-6 whorls. Fig. 243 . . . .*Euconulus fulvus* (Müller)

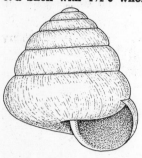

WIDTH: 3.1-3.4. mm. RANGE: Holarctic in
distribution, but absent from the southern states from North Carolina to Texas.

Shell cinnamon to pale brown, glossy,
thin and fragile; minutely perforate or imperforate. The periphery is rounded or
weakly angular. The lip is thin, and is
dilated at the columellar margin.

Fig. 243. *Euconulus fulvus* (Müller).

57b Shell with 6-8 whorls. Fig. 244........*Euconulus chersinus* (Say)**

WIDTH: 2.4-3.4 mm. RANGE: Maine to
Florida, west to Michigan and Texas.

Shell yellowish-white. The shell of this
species is very similar to that of *E. fulvus*
(Fig. 243), but has a more elevated spire,
more numerous and narrower whorls, and a
narrower aperture. It is less glossy and
is more finely sculptured than *E. fulvus.*

Fig. 244. *Euconulus chersinus* (Say).

58a Shell 2 mm. or more in diameter...........................59

**58b Shell less than 1.5 mm. in diameter. Fig. 245.................
....***Guppya sterkii* (Dall)**

WIDTH: 1.2-1.3 mm. RANGE: New York
to Florida, west to Ohio and Louisiana.

Shell with 3½-4 whorls; yellowish,
translucent; sculptured with minute,
moderately spaced spiral striae and
weak growth wrinkles. The base of
the shell is flattened and imperforate;
the periphery is rounded.

Fig. 245. *Guppya sterkii* (Dall).

59a Shell surface smooth. Fig. 246........*Guppya miamiensis* Pilsbry**

WIDTH: 2.3-2.4 mm. RANGE: Florida.

Shell with 4 whorls; pale brown,
glossy. The shell of this species is
very similar to *G. gundlachi* (Fig. 247)
in size, shape and color, but differs
by its lack of spiral sculpture.

Fig. 246. *Guppya miamiensis* Pilsbry.

59b Shell surface spirally striate. Fig. 247..*Guppya gundlachi* (Pfeiffer)

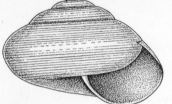

WIDTH: 3 mm. RANGE: Florida and Texas.

Shell with 4½-5 whorls; pale brown, glossy. The sculpturing of the shell is very similar to *G. sterkii* (Fig. 245). *G. gundlachi* differs from *G. sterkii* by its size and color, its subangular periphery, and its less circular aperture.

Fig. 247. *Guppya gundlachi* (Pfeiffer).

60a Shell very tightly coiled (see Fig. 200, b), usually with 6 or more flattened or shouldered whorls; last whorl usually containing teeth or lamellae. Genus *Paravitrea* (in part).......................61

60b Shell less tightly coiled (see Fig. 200, a), usually with less than 6 rounded whorls; last whorl usually without teeth..............66

61a Umbilicus wide, 1/3 or more the shell diameter. Fig. 248........ ....*Paravitrea roundyi* Morrison

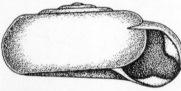

WIDTH: 1.5 mm. RANGE: Oklahoma.

Shell with 4 whorls; whitish; smooth. The whorls are rather sharply shouldered. This species is very similar to *Hawaiia minuscula* (see Fig. 254), but may be distinguished by the teeth in the aperture.

Fig. 248. *Paravitrea roundyi* Morrison (after Morrison).

61b Umbilicus narrow, 1/5 or less the shell diameter...............62

62a Shell sculptured with regularly spaced transverse lines or grooves 63

62b Shell sculptured with irregularly spaced transverse lines or grooves. Fig. 249.............................*Paravitrea reesei* Morrison

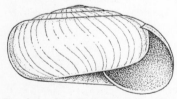

WIDTH: 3.5-4.7 mm. RANGE: Virginia and West Virginia.

Shell with 6-6½ whorls; corneous, glossy. A single radial row of three teeth are visible through the base of the shell. This species is very simi-

Fig. 249. *Paravitrea reesei* Morrison.

lar to *P. capsella* (see Fig. 268), but the last whorl is more depressed.

63a Shell with spirial striae..**64**

63b Shell without spiral striae...**65**

64a Umbilicus smaller, about 1/6 or less the shell diameter. Fig. 250.
...................................*Paravitrea walkeri* (Pilsbry)

WIDTH: 2.9-3.6 mm. RANGE: North
Carolina and Tennessee.
　Shell with 5½-6½ whorls; corneous with a cinnamon tinge. The
shell surface is dull and minutely
decussate. The adult shell is without teeth in the last whorl.

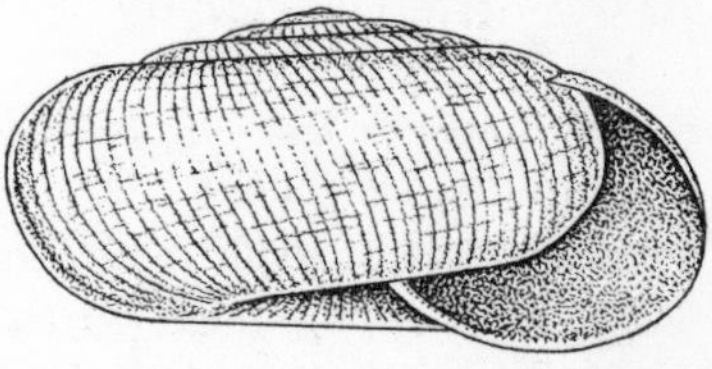

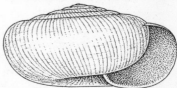

Fig. 250. *Paravitrea walkeri* (Pilsbry).

64b Umbilicus larger, about 1/5 or more the shell diameter. Fig. 251.
...................................*Paravitrea variabilis* Baker

WIDTH: 3.5-3.6 mm. RANGE: Tennessee.
　Shell with about 6½ whorls; corneous with a cinnamon tinge. This
species is similar to *P. walkeri* (Fig.
250) but is more polished, without
distinct, raised growth-wrinkles, and
the impressed transverse lines are
more widely and irregularly spaced.

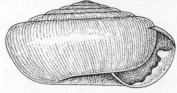

Fig. 251. *Paravitrea variabilis* Baker.

**65a Shell 3 mm. or less in diameter; umbilicus 1/7 or more the shell
diameter. Fig. 252**..............*Paravitrea multidentata* (Binney)

WIDTH: 2.5-3 mm. RANGE: Maine
to North Carolina, west to Michigan and Alabama.
　Shell with 6 whorls; corneous,
smooth, glossy; growth lines barely
visible. Two to four radiating,
transverse rows of very small, white
teeth may be seen through the base
of the shell.

Fig. 252. *Paravitrea multidentata* (Binney).

65b Shell 3.5 mm. or more in diameter; umbilicus 1/10 or less the shell diameter. Fig. 253 .... *Paravitrea lamellidens* (Pilsbry)

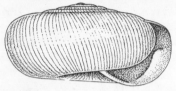

Fig. 253. *Paravitrea lamellidens* (Pilsbry).

WIDTH: 3.5-3.8 mm. RANGE: North Carolina and Tennessee.

Shell with 6½ whorls; dark reddish-brown to cinnamon buff. This species is very similar to *P. multidentata* (Fig. 252), but has one to three obliquely radial laminae instead of rows of teeth in the last whorl.

66a Shell white, opaque. Fig. 254 .... *Hawaiia minuscula* (Binney)

WIDTH: 2-2.8 mm. RANGE: United States generally.

Shell with 3½-4½ whorls; pale gray; sculptured with uneven, but distinct, growth wrinkles. It is umbilicate, the umbilicus about 1/3 the shell diameter.

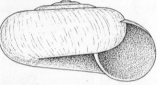

Fig. 254. *Hawaiia minuscula* (Binney).

66b Shell corneous, translucent **67**

67a Shell widely umbilicate, umbilicus about 1/3 the shell diameter. Fig. 255 .... *Pilsbryna tridens* Morrison

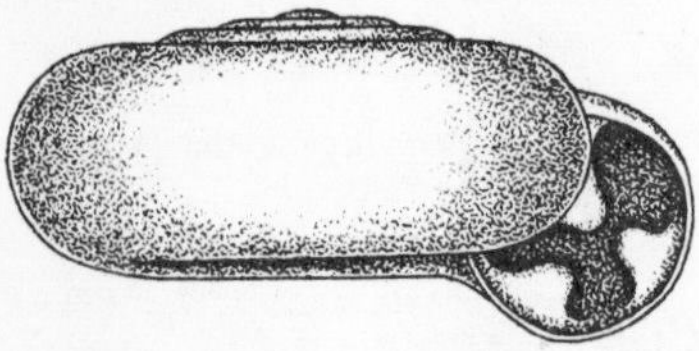

WIDTH: 1.6 mm. RANGE: Oklahoma and Texas.

Shell with 4 whorls; whitish to corneous; growth lines not prominent, irregularly spaced. The aperture is roundly-lunate and greatly constricted by the three teeth. The lip is sharp and simple.

Fig. 255. *Pilsbryna tridens* Morrison (after Morrison).

67b Shell more narrowly umbilicate, umbilicus 1/5 or less the shell diameter **68**

68a Whorls more rapidly expanding (see Fig. 200, a), the last one rather prominent. Fig. 256 .... *Pilsbryna castanea* Baker

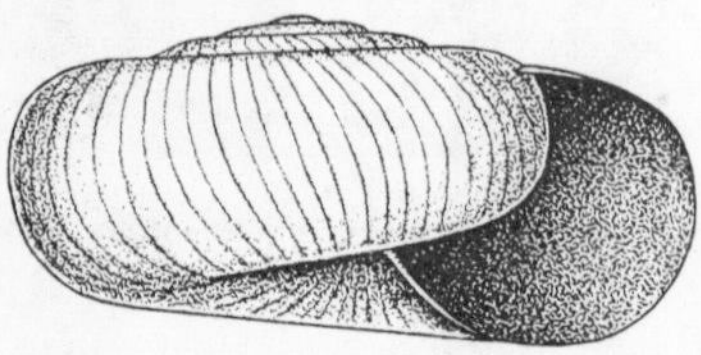

WIDTH: 3.6-3.7 mm. RANGE: Tennessee.

Shell with about 5½ whorls; yellowish. This species is similar to *P. aurea* (Fig. 257), but has a larger umbilicus and the lamellae of the body whorl (usually not present in adults) have a different arrangement.

Fig. 256. *Pilsbryna castanea* Baker.

68b Whorls more gradually expanding (see Fig. 200, b)...........69

69a Umbilicus deep and steep-sided, penultimate whorl not prominent within the umbilicus; 4½-6 whorls. Fig. 257..*Pilsbryna aurea* Baker

WIDTH: 1.7-3.3 mm. RANGE: Tennessee.

Shell yellow-corneous. The shell of this species is superficially like that of *Paravitrea capsella* (see Fig. 268) and in sculpture like that of *Zonitoides arboreus* (see Fig. 289). It differs from both of those species by its peculiar apertural lamellae.

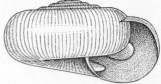

Fig. 257. *Pilsbryna aurea* Baker (after Baker).

69b Umbilicus relatively shallow, prominently showing the penultimate whorl; 3½-4 whorls. Fig. 258...............*Striatura ferrea* Morse

WIDTH: 2.5-3.4 mm. RANGE: Maine to North Carolina, west to Michigan and Tennessee.

Shell grayish, translucent, rather dull. The rapid increase in whorl size in this species is very similar to that characteristic of *Retinella* (p. 95 ff.). The animal is colored dark blue or black.

Fig. 258. *Striatura ferrea* Morse.

70a Aperture not calloused within; shell usually with more than 5 whorls; body whorl often containing one or more transverse lamellae or rows of teeth (Fig 259, b), which may be seen through the base of the translucent shell. Subfamily Zonitinae (in part). Genus *Paravitrea* (in part).........................71

70b Aperture may or may not have an internal callus (Fig. 259, a), but if a callus is absent the shell has few whorls, (4½ or less); if lamellae or teeth are present within the body whorl they are not transversely situated. Subfamily Gastrodontinae (in part)......82

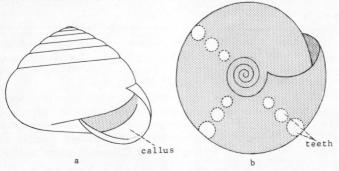

a

b

Fig. 259. a) Apertural view of shell showing callus. b) Basal view of shell with teeth visible through the last whorl.

71a Shell sculptured with regularly spaced transverse lines or grooves. Fig. 260........................... *Paravitrea clappi* (Pilsbry)

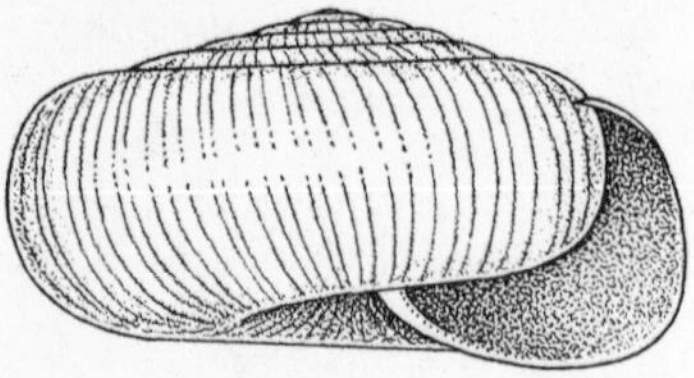

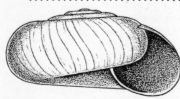

WIDTH: 5.8 mm. RANGE: North Carolina and Tennessee.

Shell with 6½-7 whorls; deep chestnut-yellow, glossy, thin, semi-transparent. The base of the shell is deeply indented around the minute umbilicus. The aperture is very narrowly lunate, its lip sharp.

Fig. 260. *Paravitrea clappi* (Pilsbry).

71b Shell sculptured with irregularly spaced transverse lines or grooves
....72

72a Whorls increasing regularly in size, the last very much wider (see Fig. 200, a)...73

72b Whorls narrow, tightly coiled, increasing very slowly in size (see Fig. 200, b)...74

73a Shell 6 mm. or less in diameter, spire slightly elevated; growth lines widely and irregularly spaced. Fig. 261.................
....................................*Paravitrea petrophila* (Bland)

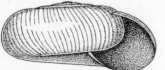

WIDTH: 5.7-6 mm. RANGE: Kentucky, Tennessee and Arkansas.

Shell with 5½-6 whorls; whitish, glossy, translucent and thin. The aperture is ovate-lunate, the peristome simple. The columellar margin is slightly reflected.

Fig. 261. *Paravitrea petrophila* (Bland).

73b Shell about 8 mm. in diameter, spire strongly depressed; growth lines closely and rather regularly spaced. Fig. 262.............
.....................*Paravitrea aulacogyra* (Pilsbry and Ferriss)

RANGE: Arkansas.

Shell with 5½-6 whorls; whitish. The shell of this species is very similar to *P. petrophila* (Fig. 261) except for its larger size, relatively smaller umbilicus and different surface sculpture.

Fig. 262. *Paravitrea aulacogyra* (Pilsbry and Ferriss) (after Pilsbry and Ferriss).

74a Species found in areas bordering or west of the Mississippi River
....**75**

74b Species found east of the Mississippi River..................**76**

75a Periphery of last whorl flattened and sloped outwards. Fig. 263..
.................................*Paravitrea significans* (Bland)

WIDTH: 4.5 mm. RANGE: Tennessee, Illinois, Arkansas and Oklahoma.

Shell with 6 whorls; light horn-colored, glossy. Adult shells are toothless, rather dome-shaped. The most distal periphery is below the middle of the last whorl. Young shells are similar to *P. capsella* (see Fig. 268) in shape.

Fig. 263. *Paravitrea significans* (Bland).

75b Periphery of last whorl rounded. Fig. 264......................
.................................*Paravitrea simpsoni* (Pilsbry)

WIDTH: 4.6-5.5 mm. RANGE: Missouri, Arkansas and Oklahoma.

Shell with 5-6 whorls; amber colored, glossy. It is similar to *P. significans* (Fig. 263) and *P. capsella* (see Fig. 268), but is more depressed, and has a wider body whorl. It also differs from *P. capsella* by its wider aperture and wider umbilicus.

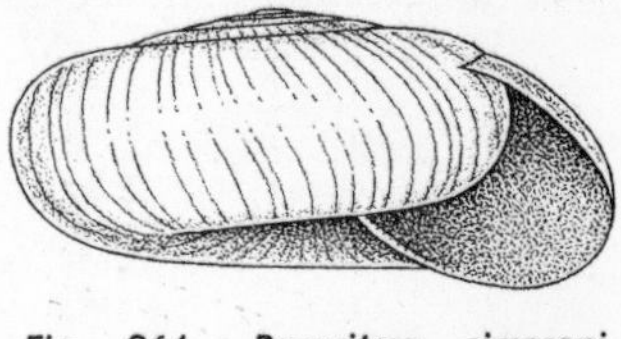

Fig. 264. *Paravitrea simpsoni* (Pilsbry).

76a Shell diameter 6.5 mm. or greater............................**77**

76b Shell diameter 6.2 mm. or less..............................**78**

77a Shell with 7-7½ whorls; adults without teeth. Fig. 265...........
.............................*Paravitrea placentula* (Shuttleworth)

WIDTH: 7.2-7.8 mm. RANGE: North Carolina, Kentucky and Tennessee.

Shell corneous, very glossy. This species is similar to *P. simpsoni* (Fig. 264), but is larger, has a relatively narrower body whorl and narrower aperture. It is also similar to

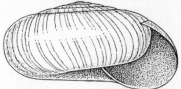

Fig. 265. *Paravitrea placentula* (Shuttleworth).

P. capsella (Fig. 268), but is larger than that species and has a smaller umbilicus.

77b Shell with 8-9 whorls; adults with or without teeth. Fig. 266.....
.....................................*Paravitrea andrewsae* (Binney)

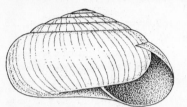

WIDTH: 6.5-8 mm. RANGE: North Carolina and Tennessee.

Shell corneous, very glossy. Teeth are usually present in the aperture and body whorl in one to several radial rows of 3 to 5 teeth each. The shell of this species is similar to *P. placentula* (Fig. 265), but the whorls increase more slowly, making the last whorl narrower.

Fig. 266. *Paravitrea andrewsae* (Binney).

78a Shell 5 mm. or more in diameter; 6½-8 whorls................79

78b Shell 4.7 mm. or less in diameter; 4½-6½ whorls..............80

79a Umbilicus relatively large, ¼ the shell diameter; adults with teeth in body whorl. Fig. 267..............*Paravitrea pilsbryana* (Clapp)

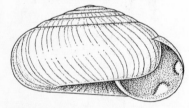

WIDTH: 5 mm. RANGE: Tennessee and Alabama.

Shell with 8 whorls; pale horn-colored, rather opaque in adults. There are 3 to 4 radial rows of relatively large, tubercular teeth visible through the base of the shell at all growth stages. The shell of this species is similar to

Fig. 267. *Paravitrea pilsbryana* (Clapp)

P. andrewsae (Fig. 266), but is smaller and has a wider umbilicus.

79b Umbilicus smaller, 1/5 or less the shell diameter; adults with or without teeth in body whorl. Fig. 268........................
.....................................*Paravitrea capsella* (Gould)

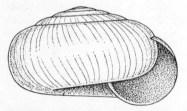

WIDTH: 4.8-6.2 mm. RANGE: Virginia and North Carolina, west to Illinois and Alabama.

Shell with 6½-7½ whorls; amber colored, glossy. The aperture is narrow, usually roundly-lunate with a simple, sharp lip. The umbilicus is small and deep.

Fig. 268. *Paravitrea capsella* (Gould).

80a Adults with teeth in body whorl. Fig. 269.....................
....*Paravitrea reesei* Morrison

WIDTH: 3.5-4.7 mm. RANGE: Virginia
and West Virginia.

Shell with 6-6½ whorls; corneous,
glossy. A single radial row of three
teeth are visible through the base of
the shell. This species is very similar
to *P. capsella* (Fig. 268), but the last
whorl is more depressed.

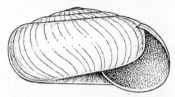

Fig. 269. *Paravitrea reesei* Morrison.

80b Adults without teeth in body whorl..........................**81**

81a Shell with 4½ whorls. Fig. 270.......*Paravitrea smithi* (Walker)

WIDTH: 4.5 mm. RANGE: Alabama.

Shell whitish, horn-colored, glossy.
The shell of this species is very similar
to *P. conecuhensis* (Fig. 271), but has
fewer whorls, a more depressed spire,
and a narrower umbilicus.

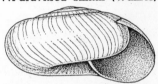

Fig. 270. *Paravitrea smithi* (Walker).

81b Shell with 6 whorls. Fig. 271......*Paravitrea conecuhensis* (Clapp)

WIDTH: 4.5 mm. RANGE: Alabama.

Shell light horn-colored, very glossy.
The shell of this species is similar to
that of *P. simpsoni* (see Fig. 264), but
shells of the same diameter have about
one more whorl, and are less depressed.

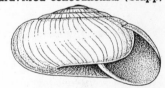

Fig. 271. *Paravitrea conecuhensis*
(Clapp).

**82a Aperture with a callous pad (see Fig. 259, a), lamellae or teeth;
5 or more whorls. Genus *Ventridens****.......................**83**

**82b Aperture without a callous pad, lamellae or teeth; shell with
5 whorls or less. Genus *Zonitoides***.......................**97**

**83a Aperture in adults with a callous pad (see Fig. 259, a), but without
teeth or lamellae**...**84**

83b Aperture in adults with lamellae or teeth....................**91**

84a Shell perforate or imperforate..............................**85**

---

*In most *Ventridens* species lamellae or teeth are present in the shell aperture or
body whorl of young individuals. In many species, however, these teeth are absorbed with continued shell growth and do not appear in adults.

84b Shell narrowly umbilicate, umbilicus ⅛ or more the shell diameter. Fig. 272. . . . .*Ventridens elliotti* (Redfield)

Fig. 272. *Ventridens elliotti* (Redfield).

WIDTH: 7.5-8.4 mm. RANGE: West Virginia and Kentucky, south to Georgia and Alabama.

Shell with 5-6 whorls; greenish horn-colored, very glossy on the base. The last whorl is slightly depressed at the aperture. The aperture is oblique and is without teeth, even in young shells. The sutures are deeply impressed.

85a Shell periphery rounded or angular **86**

85b Shell periphery sharply carinate. Fig. 273. . . . .
. . . .*Ventridens intertextus eutropis* Pilsbry

WIDTH: 14.5-15 mm. RANGE: Tennessee.

Shell with 5½-6 whorls; yellowish-horn to olive-buff, dull, marked with spiral striae. The color and surface sculpture of the shell is like that of *V. intertextus* (Fig. 274).

Fig. 273. *Ventridens intertextus eutropis* Pilsbry.

86a Shell large, generally more than 11 mm. in diameter **87**

86b Shell smaller, generally less than 11 mm. in diameter **89**

87a Shell with well-developed spiral striae; surface dull. Fig. 274. . . . .
. . . .*Ventridens intertextus* (Binney)

WIDTH: 8-20 mm. RANGE: New York to Florida, west to Michigan and Texas.

Shell with 5-6½ whorls; yellowish-horn to olive-buff. The base is whiter than the rest of the shell. The umbilical opening varies in diameter from about 1 mm. to almost closed. The whorls of young shells are angular.

Fig. 274. *Ventridens intertextus* (Binney).

87b Shell with poorly developed striae; surface glossy **88**

88a Shell very glossy; 7-8 whorls. Fig. 275..*Ventridens acerra* (Lewis)
WIDTH: 12.6-18.4 mm. RANGE: Virginia and Kentucky, south to Georgia and Alabama.
Shell light yellowish-olive. The shell is convexly conic with a somewhat flattened base. It is very similar to *V. demissus* (see Fig. 279), but is larger. Young specimens have no teeth.

Fig. 275. *Ventridens acerra* (Lewis).

88b Shell only moderately glossy; 6-7 whorls. Fig. 276..............
....*Ventridens ligera* (Say)
WIDTH: 11-15.6 mm. RANGE: New York to Florida, west to Michigan and Oklahoma.
Shell pale yellowish-horn. This species resembles *V. acerra* (Fig. 275), but is usually higher, is less widely excavated around the umbilicus and has more narrowly spaced striae. *V. ligera* is somewhat similar to *V. intertextus* (Fig. 274) in shape but is lighter in color.

Fig. 276. *Ventridens ligera* (Say).

89a Shell markedly concave at its base. Fig. 277..................
..............*Ventridens gularis theloides* (Walker and Pilsbry)
WIDTH: 7.5-8 mm. RANGE: North Carolina, Georgia and Alabama.
Shell with 7½-8 whorls; yellowish. The adult shell differs from that of *V. gularis, s. s.* (see Fig. 282), in being toothless, being more widely umbilicate, and having a more excavated base. It differs from *V. lawae* (see Fig. 285) by its much narrower umbilicus.

Fig. 277. *Ventridens gularis theloides* (Walker and Pilsbry).

89b Shell perforate, but not markedly concave at its base........90

90a Spire elevated. Fig. 278.........*Ventridens percallosus* (Pilsbry)

Fig. 278. *Ventridens percallosus* (Pilsbry).

WIDTH: 8.4-10 mm. RANGE: Tennessee.

Shell with 7-7½ whorls; pale yellow-horn colored. Its shell is similar to *V. collisella* (Fig. 281), but has a smoother upper surface. It also resembles *V. ligera* (Fig. 276), but is smaller and has a heavier callus in the aperture. Young shells have an outer-basal lamina in the aperture and a short callus on the columella.

90b Spire lower. Fig. 279..............*Ventridens demissus* (Binney)

Fig. 279. *Ventridens demissus* (Binney).

WIDTH: 7.5-11 mm. RANGE: Pennsylvania to Florida, west to Michigan and Texas.

Shell with 6-7½ whorls; horn-yellow, glossy. Typical specimens are 9 mm. or less in diameter, quite depressed, and minutely perforate. Young shells have a well-developed outer-basal lamina.

91a Shell perforate or imperforate....................................92
91b Shell narrowly umbilicate, umbilicus 1/9 or more the shell diameter 94
92a Transverse sculpture of upper surface of shell sharp and distinct 93
92b Transverse sculpture of upper surface of shell weaker, raised lines rounded. Fig. 280..............*Ventridens cerinoideus* (Anthony)

Fig. 280. *Ventridens cerinoideus* (Anthony).

WIDTH: 7.2-9 mm. RANGE: North Carolina south to Florida and Alabama.

Shell with 6½-7 whorls; waxy horn-colored, semi-translucent, glossy, marked with fine growth lines. Its spire is generally somewhat lower than that of *V. gularis* (Fig. 282). *V. cerinoideus* is generally restricted to the Coastal Plain.

93a Shell without spiral striae. Fig. 281.. *Ventridens collisella* (Pilsbry)

WIDTH: 8.4-9.6 mm. RANGE: Virginia, Tennessee and Alabama.

Shell with 7½ whorls; pale yellowish-horn, glossy. The upper shell surface is sharply defined with irregular growth wrinkles. These wrinkles are stronger toward the suture.

Fig. 281. *Ventridens collisella* (Pilsbry).

93b Shell with rather poorly developed, but distinct spiral striae. Fig. 282......................................*Ventridens gularis* (Say)

WIDTH: 7.5-9 mm. RANGE: Pennsylvania and Indiana, south to Georgia and Alabama.

Shell with 6½-8 whorls; pale yellowish-horn, very glossy. It is very similar to *V. collisella* (Fig. 281), but differs by the lower surface sculpture. It differs from *V. cerinoideus* (Fig. 280) by its larger and rougher shell.

Fig. 282. *Ventridens gularis* (Say).

**94a Umbilicus 1/9 to 1/8 the shell diameter. Fig. 283..............
....................................*Ventridens suppressus* (Say)**

WIDTH: 5.4-7.8 mm. RANGE: New York to Alabama, west to Michigan and Kentucky.

Shell with 5½-7 whorls; pale horn, glossy, semi-transparent. *V. suppressus* is smaller than related species (i.e., those with apertural teeth in the adult stage).

Fig. 283. *Ventridens suppressus* (Say).

94b Umbilicus 1/7 or more the shell diameter.....................95

95a Umbilicus 1/7 to 1/6 the shell diameter; shell 6.5-6.7 mm. in diameter. Fig. 284.....................*Ventridens coelaxis* (Pilsbry)

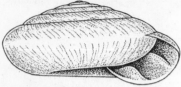

Fig. 284. *Ventridens coelaxis* (Pilsbry).

RANGE: North Carolina.

Shell with 6½-7 whorls; yellowish-corneous, semi-transparent; thin and fragile. The periphery is subangular. This species is similar to *V. lawae* (Fig. 285), but is smaller and thinner. *V. lasmodon* (Fig. 286) has a larger umbilicus.

95b Umbilicus 1/5 or more the shell diameter; shell 7.5 mm. or more in diameter **96**

96a Umbilicus 1/5 the shell diameter; shell 7.8-9 mm. in diameter. Fig. 285...................................*Ventridens lawae* (Binney)

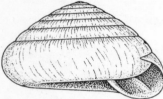

Fig. 285. *Ventridens lawae* (Binney).

RANGE: North Carolina and Tennessee.

Shell with 7½-8½ whorls; light horn to yellow, glossy. The last whorl is well rounded, not angular or subangular as in *V. coelaxis* (Fig. 284). The umbilicus is rather wide and deep with nearly parallel sides.

96b Umbilicus 1/4 to 1/3 the shell diameter; shell 7.5-7.8 mm. in diameter. Fig. 286..................*Ventridens lasmodon* (Phillips)

Fig. 286. *Ventridens lasmodon* (Phillips).

RANGE: Tennessee and Alabama.

Shell with 7½-8 whorls; pale whitish-horn, glossy; rather thick. This species is the most widely umbilicate of the *Ventridens*. The shell has well-rounded whorls, which are distinctly wrinkled above, weakly wrinkled below.

97a Shell moderately to widely umbilicate, umbilicus 1/5 or more the shell diameter **98**

**97b Shell narrowly umbilicate, umbilicus 1/6 or less the shell diameter.
Fig. 287.............................*Paravitrea smithi* (Walker)**

WIDTH: 4.5 mm. RANGE: Alabama.

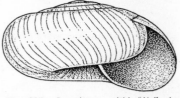

Shell with about 4½ whorls; whitish, horn-colored, glossy. The shell of this species is very similar to *P. conecuhensis* (see Fig. 271), but has fewer whorls, a more depressed spire, and a narrower umbilicus.

Fig. 287. *Paravitrea smithi* (Walker).

98a Shell glossy and rather weakly sculptured; moderately umbilicate, umbilicus 1/5 to 1/4 the shell diameter......................99

98b Shell dull, with distinct, rather coarse sculpture; rather widely umbilicate, umbilicus 1/4 or more the shell diameter............100

99a Shell larger, more than 6 mm. in diameter, without faint spiral striae. Fig. 288........................*Zonitoides nitidus* (Müller)

WIDTH: 6-7 mm. RANGE: Maine to Maryland, west to Washington and California.

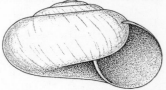

Shell with 4½-5 whorls; olive-yellow, semi-transparent, very glossy. The gradually widening whorls are separated by an impressed suture. The aperture is roundly- to ovate-lunate, its columellar margin slightly expanded.

Fig. 288. *Zonitoides nitidus* (Müller).

99b Shell smaller, 6 mm. or less in diameter, usually with faint spiral striae. Fig. 289........................*Zonitoides arboreus* (Say)

WIDTH: 5-6 mm. RANGE: Reported from all the states, except Nevada.

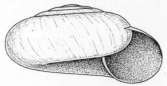

Shell with 4½-5 whorls; olive buff. This species is very similar to *Z. nitidus* (Fig. 288), but is smaller, more depressed, more widely umbilicate, has a less convex base and the aperture is more oval.

Fig. 289. *Zonitoides arboreus* (Say).

100a Shell 5 mm. or more in diameter; upper lip margin flattened and deflected. Fig. 290...............*Zonitoides patuloides* (Pilsbry)

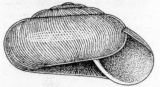

Fig. 290. *Zonitoides patuloides* (Pilsbry).

WIDTH: 5-5.8 mm. RANGE: North Carolina and Tennessee.

Shell with 4½-5 whorls; light green, dull, not transparent. This species is less depressed and less coarsely sculptured than *Z. limatulus* (Fig. 292) and *Z. lateumbilicatus* (Fig. 291).

100b Shell 5 mm. or less in diameter; upper lip margin rounded and not reflected 101

101a Shell depressed and greatly flattened; umbilicus more than 1/3 the shell diameter. Fig. 291...*Zonitoides lateumbilicatus* (Pilsbry)

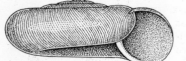

Fig. 291. *Zonitoides lateumbilicatus* (Pilsbry).

WIDTH: 4.2-5 mm. RANGE: Kentucky, Tennessee and Alabama.

Shell with about 4½ whorls; white to corneous. The shell of this species is similar to the more northern *Z. limatulus* (Fig. 292), but is more depressed, more widely umbilicate, and its base has stronger growth lines.

101b Shell depressed but not especially flattened; umbilicus 1/4 to 1/3 the shell diameter. Fig. 292....*Zonitoides limatulus* (Binney)

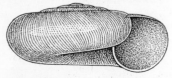

Fig. 292. *Zonitoides limatulus* (Binney).

WIDTH: 4.3-5 mm. RANGE: New York, Indiana, Illinois and Missouri.

Shell with about 4½ whorls; white to corneous, dull, not transparent. It is greatly depressed, rather widely umbilicate. The growth lines are more distinct on the top of the shell than those on the base.

TESTACELLIDAE

This family consists of slug-like snails, which bear a small rudimentary shell near their posterior end. The family is not native to North America. The European *Testacella haliotidea* has been reported several times in the United States. It is a carnivorous species, preying on soil invertebrates.

Figs. 293, 294......................*Testacella haliotidea* **Draparnaud**

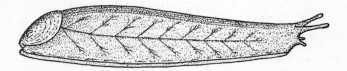

Fig. 293. Animal and shell of *Testacella haliotidea* Draparnaud.

LENGTH: 6-10 mm. RANGE: Introduced into greenhouses in Pennsylvania, Illinois, Tennessee, Oregon and California.

Shell depressed, ear-shaped, imperforate, and with a subspiral, posterior nucleus. The surface is rugosely striate. The apex is very small and short and is not separated from the columellar margin. The aperture is oval. The animal tapers anteriorly, and is much too large to retract into its shell. It spends much time in the ground, and in its native countries apparently feeds chiefly on earthworms.

Fig. 294. Ventral view of shell of *Testacella haliotidea* Draparnaud.

HAPLOTREMATIDAE

This is mainly a North American family, but a few members inhabit the West Indies, Latin America, and northern South America. The family contains only one genus, *Haplotrema*, which is best represented in the western United States. The shell is very compressed and widely umbilicate, usually light greenish-yellow in color.

Fig. 295.................................*Haplotrema concavum* **(Say)**

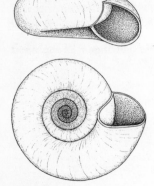

WIDTH: 16-22 mm. RANGE: Maine to Florida, west to Iowa and Arkansas.

Shell with 4½-5½ whorls. It resembles some of the shells of the Zonitidae, but is either more discoidal or has a wider umbilicus than any zonitid species of similar size. *H. concavum* is carnivorous in habit, feeding on the other land snails.

Fig. 295. Apertural and umbilical views of the shell of *Haplotrema concavum* (Say).

STREPTAXIDAE

This family is not native to North America, but is represented in our fauna by the introduced *Gulella bicolor*, a species originally from the Orient. Shells of this family are heliciform, cylindrical, or sometimes pupa-shaped. The aperture lip is expanded; the columella is always thickened and usually toothed.

Fig. 296....................................*Gulella bicolor* **(Hutton)**

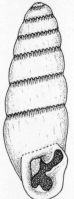

LENGTH: 7 mm. RANGE: Introduced into Florida.

Shell with 6-7 whorls, white, polished and smooth, except at the sutures, where the shell is ribbed. The aperture contains four teeth: a parietal lamella, a subconically shaped lamella on the right margin, a small basal tooth and a deep-seated columellar lamella.

Fig. 296. *Gulella bicolor* (Hutton).

OLEACINIDAE

This is a family of the Mediterranean region and tropical and subtropical America. Its species usually have rather large shells that are higher than wide, with narrowly ovate-lunate apertures and truncate or twisted columellae. They are very active predators which feed on other land snails.

1a Shell small, less than 10 mm. long, conical, ribbed, with strongly flattened whorls. Fig. 297.....*Varicella gracillima floridana* Pilsbry

LENGTH: 6-7.5 mm. RANGE: Florida.

Shell with 8-8½ whorls; corneous to pale brown; thin, very slender, imperforate. The sutures are deeply impressed. The shell sculpture consists of narrow, nearly straight, axial ribs, and more numerous parallel growth lines.

Figure 297. *Varicella gracillima floridana* Pilsbry.

1b Shell large, more than 20 mm. long, fusiform; whorls rounded to moderately flattened, but not strongly flattened. Genus *Euglandina*
....2
2a Shell more than 35 mm. long; color pinkish or some shade of brown or tan...3
2b Shell less than 35 mm. long; color whitish. Fig. 298............
...................................*Euglandina texasiana* (Pfeiffer)

LENGTH: 29-32 mm. RANGE: Texas.

Shell with ˉ6½ whorls; whitish, sometimes with a faint pink cast, glossy. The first three whorls are smooth; the rest are sculptured with regular growth lines. Spiral striae are absent or sub-obsolete. The aperture is nearly half the shell length.

Figure 298. *Euglandina teaesiana* (Pfeiffer).

3a Shell thick, with prominent growth lines, without spiral striae; color pinkish-white. Fig. 299..............._Euglandina rosea_ (Férussac)

LENGTH: 50-76 mm. RANGE: South Carolina, Florida, Alabama, Mississippi and Louisiana.

Shell with 6-7 whorls; pinkish. The shell of this species is somewhat similar to that of *E. texasiana* (Fig. 298), but is larger, more pinkish in color, and has more prominent growth lines.

Figure 299. dfetaish
na rosea (Ferussac).

3b Shell rather thin, spirally striate; growth lines not prominent. Color tan or brown. Fig. 300............_Euglandina singleyana_ (Binney)

LENGTH: 40-52 mm. RANGE: Texas.

Shell with 6½-7½ whorls; pale brown, glossy. The shell of this species is similar to the shells of *E. rosea* (Fig. 299) and *E. texasiana* (Fig. 298), but differs from them in size, color, sculpture and gloss. This snail is most often found under dead wood or stones.

Figure 300. Eugland-
na singleyana (Bin-
ney).

ACHATINIDAE

The Achatinidae are a large group of mainly tropical snails, which vary greatly in size from the rather large *Rumina decollata* to the minute *Cecilioides*. The shell is usually long and thin, without internal lamellae. Its base may be either perforate or imperforate. The base of the columella is either straight or truncate.

1a Spire partly broken off in adult shells. Fig. 301. . . . .
. . . .*Rumina decollata* **(Linne)**

LENGTH: 25-45 mm. RANGE: Introduced into the southern United States and occurring from North Carolina to Florida, west to Texas.

In adult shells only 4-7 whorls remain, the other
8-10 having been lost by successive breakages. The
shell is perforate, glossy and sculptured with fine
spiral striae. The whorls are only slightly rounded,
the sutures are not impressed. The columella is
straight, its lip margin reflexed. The lip is solid and
not reflected.

Figure 301. *Rumina decollata* (Linné).

1b Spire normally not broken off 2

2a Base of columella truncate (see Fig. 13, i); shell imperforate 3

**2b Base of columella straight (see Fig. 13, j), not truncate; shell per-
forate** 5

**3a Shell small, adults (with 5-6 whorls) less than 6 mm. long; very
glossy; shell surface smooth or only very weakly striate. Genus
*Cecilioides*** 4

**3b Shell larger, adults more than 6 mm. long; moderately glossy; shell
surface striate. Fig. 302.** . . . .*Subulina octona* **(Bruguière)**

LENGTH: 17-18 mm. RANGE: Introduced into Florida.
Occasionally reported from greenhouses in the northern states.

Shell with 9-11 whorls. Shell surface glossy, transversely wrinkled; sutures impressed; aperture small,
oval, slightly lunate. It is similar to *Opeas* (pp. 125,
126) and *Lamellaxis* (pp. 125-127), except that it is larger,
perforate, and the columella is truncate.

Figure 302. *Subulina octona* (Bruguière).

4a Base of columella moderately truncate; callus present on parietal wall; whorls convex; shell surface smooth. Fig. 303.............
......................................*Cecilioides aperta* (Swainson)

LENGTH: 4-5 mm. RANGE: Introduced into New Jersey, Virginia and Florida.

Shell with 5-6 whorls. The whorls are moderately rounded; the apex is round and blunt. The aperture is narrowly ovate-lunate, the columella slightly truncate, the lip sharp and not reflected. The animal has two pairs of tentacles but lacks eyes.

Figure 303. *Cecilioi-des aperta* (Swain-son).

4b Base of columella abruptly truncate; no callus on parietal wall; whorls nearly flat-sided; shell surface weakly striate. Fig. 304....
......................................*Cecilioides acicula* (Müller)

LENGTH: 4-5 mm. RANGE: Introduced into Pennsylvania and Florida.

Shell with 5-6 whorls. It is very similar to *C. aperta* (Fig. 303), except for the key characters mentioned above. Both species are ground dwellers that are transferred from place to place on the roots of tropical plants.

Figure 304. *Cecilioi-des acicula* (Mül-ler).

5a Shell surface sculptured with raised axial ribs; aperture length less than ¼ the shell height. Fig. 305....*Lamellaxis micra* (d'Orbigny)

LENGTH: 7 mm. RANGE: Introduced into Florida.

Shell with 6½ whorls. This species differs from other species of *Lamellaxis* and *Opeas* by having widely spaced transverse ribs, a bullet-shaped spire, smaller aperture, and shorter whorls.

Figure 305. *Lamellaxis micra* (d'Orbigny).

5b Shell surface without raised axial ribs; aperture length more than ¼ the shell height...**6**

6a Sutures distinctly crenulate (i.e., undulated or scalloped, see Fig. 12, d). Fig. 306...........*Opeas pyrgula* Schmacker and Boettger

LENGTH: 8 mm. RANGE: Introduced into Pennsylvania and Virginia.

Shell with about 7 whorls, elongate with high tapering spire, the surface sculptured with weak, irregular, transverse lines or wrinkles. The aperture is ovate-lunate, the outer lip thin, not reflected, and rounded. The columella is straight or slightly concave, but not truncated.

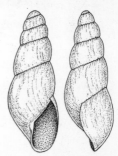

Figure 306. *Opeas pyrgula* Schmacker and Boettger.

6b Sutures straight or only very slightly crenulate...................**7**

7a Upper lip strongly retracted to the suture (see Fig. 13, h). Fig. 307. .
. . . .*Opeas pumilum* (Pfeiffer)

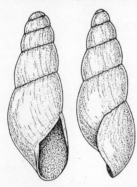

LENGTH: 5-6 mm. RANGE: Introduced into Florida and found in greenhouses in Pennsylvania and Illinois.

Shell with about 6½ whorls. It is very similar to O. *pyrgula* (Fig. 306), except for the key characters mentioned above.

Figure 307. *Opeas pumilum* (Pfeiffer).

7b Upper lip straight or only moderately retracted at the suture. 8

8a Shell heavily striate; not glossy. Fig. 308. . . . .
. . . . *Lamellaxis gracilis* (Hutton)

LENGTH: 10 mm. RANGE: Introduced into the southeastern United States.

Shell with 8 whorls, small, very high spired, perforate, and with a relatively dull surface and rather heavy growth lines. It has a straight outer lip and expanded columellar lip.

Figure 308. *Lamellaxis gracilis* (Hutton).

8b Shell moderately to weakly striate; glossy. .9

9a Shell very glossy; weakly striate. Fig. 309.....................
....*Lamellaxis mauritianus* (Pfeiffer)

LENGTH: 11.5 mm. RANGE: Found in a number of greenhouses in the United States.

Shell with 6½-7 whorls. This species is similar to *L.
clavulinus* (Fig. 310), but differs from both it and *L.
gracilis* (Fig. 308) by its more glossy surface and weaker
transverse striation.

Figure 309. *Lamel-
laxis mauritianus*
(Pfeiffer).

9b Shell moderately glossy; moderately striate. Fig. 310............
.........................*Lamellaxis clavulinus* (Potiez and Michaud)

LENGTH: 7 mm. RANGE: Introduced into greenhouses
in Pennsylvania.

Shell with 7 whorls, moderately glossy and with
moderately developed growth lines. Its whorls are rounded, the sutures straight. The aperture is ovate-lunate,
its length 1/4-1/3 the shell length.

Figure 310. *Lamel-
laxis clavulinus* (Po-
tiez and Michaud).

UROCOPTIDAE

This is a large, mainly tropical family with few species in the
United States. It is native to the Western Hemisphere and apparently
related to the Bulimulidae and the Achatinidae. The shell is very
elongate, with a characteristically tapering spire, which tends to lose
its taper near the apex. The apertural lip is expanded, often strongly
reflected.

1a Shell imperforate 2

**1b Shell narrowly umbilicate. Subfamily Holospirinae. Genus *Holo-
spira*** 4

2a Shell slender, the early whorls usually broken off in adult shells. Subfamily Urocoptinae. Fig. 311.. *Cochlodinella poeyana* **(d'Orbigny)**

LENGTH: 9.5-14 mm. RANGE: Florida.

Shells with broken spires usually have 7½-9 whorls. Rare shells with unbroken spires may have up to 19½ whorls and measure up to 15.5 mm. in length. The shell is typically colored uniformly white or light gray, but is sometimes mottled with brownish or white markings.

Figure 311. *Cochlodinella poeyana* (d'-Orbigny)

2b Shell wider, the early whorls retained in adult shells. Subfamily Microceraminae. Genus *Microceramus* **3**

3a Shell larger, more than 8 mm. in length. Fig. 312 .... *Microceramus pontificus* **(Gould)**

LENGTH: 8.3-12 mm. RANGE: Florida and Texas.

Shell with 9-11 whorls; white to cream or pale brown, mottled with darker brown; sculptured with rather coarse transverse striae. The sutures are crenulated, bordered with white shell deposits.

Figure 312. *Microceramus pontificus* (Gould).

3b Shell smaller, less than 8 mm. in length. Fig. 313 . . . .
. . . . *Microceramus floridanus* **(Pilsbry)**

LENGTH: 5.5-7.8 mm. RANGE: Florida.

Shell with 8-10 whorls; white to cream or pale brown, marked with darker brown blotches. The shell of this species is very similar to *M. pontificus* (Fig. 312), but is smaller, usually has finer surface sculpture, and the white sutural deposits are somewhat lower and less regularly spaced.

Figure 313. *Microceramus floridanus* (Pilsbry).

4a Last whorl distorted, sometimes making the shell appear whorled to the left; surface relatively smooth. Fig. 314 . . . .
. . . . *Holospira roemeri* **(Pfeiffer)**

LENGTH: 8.5-18.5 mm. RANGE: Texas and New Mexico.

Shell with 10-17 whorls; pale brown, rather glossy, smooth except for faint growth lines. The aperture is oval, usually with a rather conspicuous fold in the right margin.

Figure 314. *Holospira roemeri* (Pfeiffer).

4b Last whorl not distorted, shell obviously dextral; surface ribbed.
Fig. 315...........................*Holospira goldfussi* (Menke)

LENGTH: 10-15 mm. RANGE: Texas.

Shell with 10½-15 whorls; pale flesh-colored. The apex is more gradually tapered than in *H. roemeri* (Fig. 314). The aperture is rounded below, flattened above with a slight fold.

Figure 315. *Holospira goldfussi* (Menke).

BULIMULIDAE

The Bulimulidae are a South American family of many species, a few of which spread into Middle America, the West Indies and the southern United States. Members of the family occur in Australia, Melanesia and New Zealand, and are thought to have reached these regions via Antarctica (Pilsbry). The shells are often large, brightly colored, and with capacious body whorls.

1a Shell large, more than 40 mm. in length; imperforate; embryonic whorls smooth. Subfamily Orthalicinae.........................2

1b Shell smaller, less than 40 mm. in length; usually perforate; embryonic whorls sculptured. Subfamily Bulimulinae..............4

2a Aperture large, its length nearly half the shell length. Genus *Orthalicus* 3

2b Aperture smaller, its length considerably less than half the shell length. Fig. 316 . . . .*Liguus fasciatus* (Müller)

LENGTH: 41-72 mm. RANGE: Florida.

Shell with 6-8 whorls; white, or more usually banded or streaked with green, brown, yellow, pink, or blue. The columella may be either straight or truncate. This tree snail feeds on fungi growing on bark.

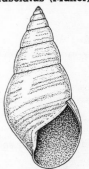

Figure 316. *Liguus fasciatus* (Müller).

3a Major color markings of shell consisting of irregular transverse stripes. Fig. 317 . . . .*Orthalicus reses* (Say)

LENGTH: 42-62 mm. RANGE: Florida.

Shell with 6-6½ whorls; white to pale buff, marked with chestnut-brown stripes. The apex is white. The interior of the aperture is colored like the outside of the shell. A subspecies with a black apex has been named *O. r. nesodryas* by Pilsbry.

Figure 317. *Orthalicus reses* (Say)

3b Major color markings of shell consisting of two or three spiral bands. Fig. 318 . . . .*Orthalicus floridensis* Pilsbry

LENGTH: 48-71 mm. RANGE: Florida.

Shell with about 6 whorls; white to cream-buff, marked with chestnut-brown stripes. The apex is dark. The interior of the aperture is white, showing the bands. The columella is white and straight.

Figure 318. *Orthalicus floridensis* Pilsbry.

4a Embryonic whorls sculptured with fine spiral puncta; shell uniform in color or with spiral color bands. Genus *Drymaeus*.......5

4b Embryonic whorls sculptured with transverse ribs; shell without spiral color bands. Genus *Bulimulus*.........................7

5a Shell thin and fragile, rather translucent.......................6

5b Shell more solid, opaque. Fig. 319....*Drymaeus multilineatus* (Say)

LENGTH: 15-24 mm. RANGE: Florida.

Shell with 6½-7 whorls; ivory yellow, with many transverse, dark reddish-brown stripes, and usually several similarly colored spiral bands; generally rather dull. This species inhabits southern Florida and lives on trees, bushes or herbaceous vegetation.

Figure 319. *Drymaeus multilineatus* (Say).

6a Shell relatively large, usually more than 25 mm. long. Fig. 320....
....................................*Drymaeus dormani* (Binney)

LENGTH: 20-32 mm. RANGE: Florida.

Shell with 6-6½ whorls; light waxy to very pale horn-colored, glossy, transparent. Color markings consist of 3-5 spiral rows of interrupted, reddish-brown patches. This species inhabits central and northern Florida.

Figure 320. *Drymaeus dormani* (Binney).

132

6b Shell smaller, less than 25 mm. long. Fig. 321...................
.....................................*Drymaeus dominicus* (Reeve)

LENGTH: 15-24 mm. RANGE: Florida.

Shell with 5-6 whorls; whitish, horn-colored, or pale buff; glossy, transparent; marked with 3-5 reddish-brown spiral color bands. Occasionally the color bands may be lacking. This species inhabits southern and eastern Florida.

Figure 321. *Drymaeus dominicus* (Reeve).

7a Shell relatively large, usually 24 mm. or more in length; solid, rather thick 8

7b Shell smaller, usually less than 24 mm. in length; rather thin. Fig. 322....................................*Bulimulus dealbatus* (Say)

LENGTH: 16.3-26 mm. RANGE: Illinois and Kentucky to Alabama, west to Kansas and New Mexico.

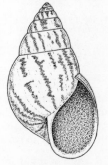

Shell with 6-7 whorls; streaked with opaque white on a brownish or gray background. The interior of the aperture is colored like the exterior of the shell. The apertural lip is dilated.

Figure 322. *Bulimulus dealbatus* (Say).

8a Interior of aperture colored dark brown. Fig. 323..............
...........................*Bulimulus alternatus mariae* (Albers)

LENGTH: 24-32 mm. RANGE: Texas.

Shell with 6-7 whorls; uniformly white or with irregular, transverse brown to gray stripes. The columellar margin is widely reflected, often toothed. This species inhabits southern Texas.

Figure 323. *Bulimulus alternatus mariae* (Albers).

8b Interior of aperture white or tan. Fig. 324.....................
...............................*Bulimulus schiedeanus* (Pfeiffer)

LENGTH: 21-39 mm. RANGE: Texas.

Shell with 7-7½ whorls; uniformly white or with some darker streaks; opaque, not glossy. The columellar margin is rather widely reflected and without teeth. This species inhabits western Texas.

Figure 324. *Bulimulus schiedeanus* (Pfeiffer).

SAGDIDAE

The Sagdidae are a family of moderate to small-sized helicid snails of the tropical and subtropical Middle American region. A few species extend into the southern United States. Their shells vary from very depressed to globose, and are of a plain, uniform color. The outer lip is thin and not expanded, while the columellar lip is generally reflected.

1a Shell without thin oblique ribs...................................2

1b Shell sculptured with thin oblique periostracal ribs. Genus *Thysanophora* 3

2a Shell 5 mm. or more in diameter, strongly shouldered. Fig. 325...
...................................*Lacteoluna selenina* (Gould)

WIDTH: 5-5.3 mm. RANGE: Florida.

Shell with 4½-5 slowly increasing whorls; bluish-white, not glossy; thin; depressed; umbilicate. Umbilicus 1/6 to 1/5 the shell diameter. The last whorl is marked with fine growth wrinkles.

Figure 325. *Lacteoluna selenina* (Gould).

2b Shell smaller, less than 4 mm. in diameter; last whorl rounded. Fig. 326.............................*Hojeda inaguensis* (Weinland)

WIDTH: 3.3-3.5 mm. RANGE Florida.

Shell with 4-4½ whorls; whitish to pale brown, dull. Umbilicus about ¼ the shell diameter. The shell of this species is somewhat similar to *Lacteoluna selenina* (Fig. 325), but is smaller, has rounded whorls and is more widely umbilicate. It lacks the periostracal ribs of *Thysanophora horni* (Fig. 329).

Figure 326. *Hojeda inaguensis* (Weinland).

3a Shell globose, the height and diameter nearly equal. Fig. 327....
.......................*Thysanophora plagioptycha* (Shuttleworth)

WIDTH: 2.5-3 mm. RANGE: Florida and Texas.

Shell with 4-4½ whorls; pale brown, semi-transparent, somewhat g l o s s y. Sculptured with faint growth lines and very oblique, sometimes interrupted, periostracal ribs. The umbilicus is 1/8 to 1/7 the shell diameter.

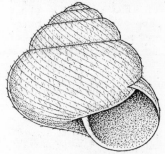

Figure 327. *Thysanophora plagioptycha* (Shuttleworth).

3b Shell depressed, the diameter much greater than the height......4

4a Shell with strongly shouldered and flattened whorls. Fig. 328....
................................*Thysanophora incrustata* (Poey)

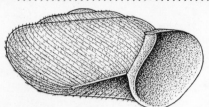

Figure 328. *Thysanophora incrustata* (Poey).

WIDTH: 3.9-4.7 mm. RANGE: Texas.

Shell with 4-5 whorls; horn-colored; depressed. The most distal periphery is situated above the middle of the last whorl giving the shell a shouldered appearance. The umbilicus is about 1/3 the shell diameter. The shell is usually incrusted with dirt, hence its name.

4b Shell with weakly shouldered and more rounded whorls. Fig. 329.
................................*Thysanophora horni* (Gabb)

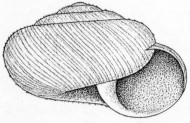

Figure 329. *Thysanophora horni* (Gabb).

WIDTH: 3.8-4.7 mm. RANGE: Texas, New Mexico and Arizona.

Shell with 4½-5 whorls; brown. The shell of this species is similar to that of *T. incrustata* (Fig. 328), but is less depressed, has more rounded whorls and a narrower umbilicus (about ¼ the shell diameter). Like *T. incrustata*, it is usually incrusted with dirt.

POLYGYRIDAE

This is a family of medium to large helicid snails with reflected lips and often with toothed apertures. Although mainly a family of temperate climates, the range of the Polygyridae extends from Alaska to eastern Canada and south into the tropics. Its species are most abundant in humid regions and are mainly woodland snails. Immature individuals are difficult to identify; the lip of their shells is not reflected and usually apertural teeth have not yet developed in dentate species.

1a Shell aperture with one, two or three teeth. Genera *Stenotrema, Polygyriscus, Polygyra, Mesodon* (in part), *Triodopsis* (in part) (see Fig. 389) 2

1b Shell aperture without teeth, or at most with only a low callus in the basal columellar curve of the lip. Genera *Allogona, Praticolella, Mesodon* (in part), *Triodopsis* (in part) (see Fig. 389).....92

2a Aperture slit-like, narrow, with a long parietal tooth, and usually with a notched basal lip* (Fig. 330). Genus *Stenotrema* 3

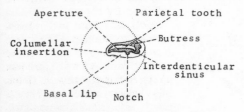

Aperture Parietal tooth

Columellar insertion

Butress

Interdenticular sinus

Basal lip Notch

Fig. 330. Apertural terminology in *Stenotrema*.

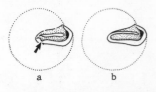

a b

Fig. 331. a, Basal lip with a notch near the columellar insertion; b, basal lip without a notch near the columellar insertion.

2b Aperture more or less round or oval; parietal tooth usually shorter; basal lip usually not notched 28

3a Shell periphery angular or carinate 4

3b Shell periphery round or only weakly angular 10

4a Shell periphery very strongly angular or carinate 5

4b Shell periphery less strongly angular; not carinate 8

5a Outer edge of basal lip free from the body whorl 6

5b Basal lip appressed to the body whorl 7

6a Shell very depressed, lens-shaped, height about ½ the diameter; basal lip with a notch near the columella. Figs. 331, a; 332 ......
...................................*Stenotrema hubrichti* Pilsbry

Figure 332. *Stenotrema hubrichti* (Pilsbry).

WIDTH: 8.9-9.7 mm. RANGE: Illinois.

Shell with 4½-5 whorls; whitish; imperforate; whorls increasing very slowly in diameter; embryonic whorls minutely granulose. The aperture is similar to *S. fraternum* (see Fig. 341), but is narrower.

*The notches in the basal lip are usually not visible when the shell is in side view because of the projecting parietal tooth.

6b Shell less strongly depressed, height more than ½ the diameter; basal lip without a notch near the columella. Figs. 331, b; 333...
...............................*Stenotrema barbigerum* (Redfield)

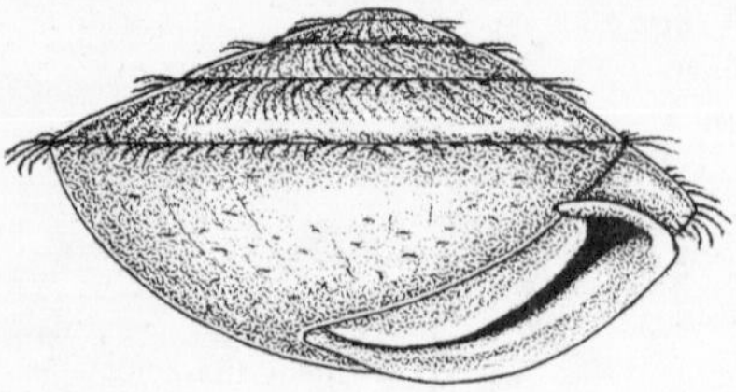

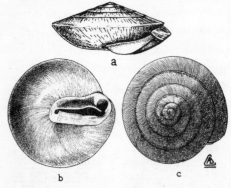

Figure 333. *Stenotrema barbigerum* (Redfield).

WIDTH: 8.7-10 mm. RANGE: North Carolina to Georgia, west to Tennessee and Alabama.

Shell with about 5 whorls; light cinnamon-colored; thick. The larger whorls are sculptured with radial periostracal ridges which extend into long hairs at the shell periphery. The base is sculptured with sparse, stout hairs.

7a Shell very depressed, lens-shaped, height less than ½ the diameter. Fig. 334............................................*Stenotrema spinosum* (Lea)

WIDTH: 11.8-15 mm. RANGE: Virginia, Georgia, Tennessee and Alabama.

Shell with 5½-6 whorls; cinnamon to cinnamon-brown; imperforate. The base of the shell is often sculptured with weak spiral striae. The parietal tooth is larger than in S. *barbigerum* (Fig. 333).

a

b   c

Figure 334. *Stenotrema spinosum* (Lea).

7b Shell less strongly depressed, height more than ½ the diameter. Fig. 335........................................*Stenotrema edgarianum* (Lea)

WIDTH: 9-10 mm. RANGE: Tennessee.

Shell with 5-5½ whorls; cinnamon-buff; imperforate. The larger whorls are sculptured with minute radial striae and narrow, radial, scattered, periostracal ridges. The base of the shell is sculptured with many short, stiff hairs.

Figure 335. *Stenotrema edgarianum* (Lea).

8a Basal lip (in basal view) with a small or indistinct notch. Fig. 336...
.....................................*Stenotrema edvardsi* (Bland)

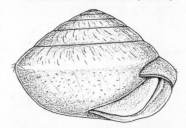

WIDTH: 7-8 mm. RANGE: Pennsylvania, south to Virginia and Tennessee.

Shell with 5-5½ whorls; tawny-olive to light cinnamon-colored; imperforate. The shell is sculptured with microscopic radial lines, larger ridges, and on the base with small hairs. The shell of this species is similar to *S. barbigerum* (Fig. 333), but is less depressed.

Figure 336. *Stenotrema edvardsi* (Bland).

8b Basal lip with a deep and well-developed notch.................9
9a Shell surface rather smooth. Fig. 337...........................
.....................................*Stenotrema labrosum* (Bland)

WIDTH: 10.5-12.7 mm. RANGE: Missouri, Arkansas, Louisiana and Oklahoma.

Shell with 5-5½ whorls; tawny-olive to snuff-brown; imperforate. The shell is sculptured with short, radial periostracal ridges and indistinct spiral striae. The apertural characters are similar to *S. stenotrema* (Fig. 358).

Figure 337. *Stenotrema labrosum* (Bland).

9b Shell surface with long periostracal hairs. Fig. 338..............
.....................................*Stenotrema pilsbryi* (Ferriss)

WIDTH: 9.2-9.8 mm. RANGE: Arkansas and Oklahoma.

Shell with 5-5½ whorls; tawny olive-colored; imperforate. The shape of the shell of this species is very similar to *S. labrosum* (Fig. 337), but the spiral rows of stiff periostracal hairs readily differentiate these two species.

Figure 338. *Stenotrema pilsbryi* (Ferriss).

10a Basal lip without a notch.....................................11

10b Basal lip with a median notch..............................13

11a Aperture with a lamella parallel to the basal lip and parietal tooth. Fig. 339....................*Stenotrema maxillatum* (Gould)

WIDTH: 6.5-7.4 mm. RANGE: Georgia and Alabama.

Shell with about 5 whorls; cinnamon-buff to cinnamon-brown; imperforate. The shell is sculptured with short, dense hairs arranged in oblique rows, the aperture is very narrow.

Figure 339. *Stenotrema maxillatum* (Gould).

11b Aperture without a lamella in addition to the parietal tooth.....12

12a Shell relatively small, 9 mm. or less in diameter. Fig. 340.......
....*Stenotrema leai* (Binney)

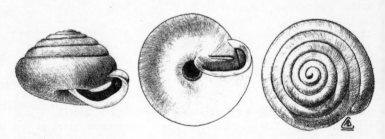

Figure 340. *Stenotrema leai* (Binney).

WIDTH: 6.1-9.4 mm. RANGE: New York to Virginia, west to South Dakota and Texas.

Shell with 5½-6½ whorls; tannish-olive to cinnamon-buff; umbilicate; somewhat glossy. Sculptured with fine growth lines, and often on the last whorl, fine hairs. This species is called *Polygyra monodon* in many older references.

12b Shell larger, 10 mm. or more in diameter. Fig. 341.............
.....................................*Stenotrema fraternum* (Say)

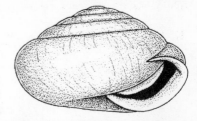

WIDTH: 7.8-11.4 mm. RANGE: New Hampshire to Georgia, west to Minnesota and Oklahoma.

Shell with 5-6 whorls; pale tan to tawny-olive or cinnamon-buff; imperforate or perforate. The shell of this species differs from *S. leai* (Fig. 340) by being more loosely coiled, having a smaller umbilicus, and a rougher surface.

Figure 341. *Stenotrema fraternum* (Say).

13a Notch in basal lip wide (Fig. 342, a, b).....................14

13b Notch in basal lip narrow (Fig. 342, c) or small and nearly obsolete 15

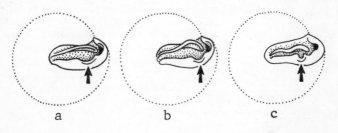

Fig. 342. Basal lip with a) very wide notch; b) moderately wide notch; c) narrow notch.

14a Notch in basal lip very wide. Figs. 342, a; 343...............
...................................*Stenotrema cohuttense* (Clapp)

WIDTH: 6-7.3 mm. RANGE: Georgia and Tennessee.

Shell with about 5 whorls; reddish horn-colored; imperforate; thin; very densely sculptured with very fine hairs. The large, erect parietal tooth terminates in a hook which passes under the lip between the lip tooth and the notch.

Figure 343. *Stenotrema cohuttense* (Clapp).

14b Notch in basal lip narrower. Figs. 342, b; 344.................
....*Stenotrema brevipila* (Clapp)

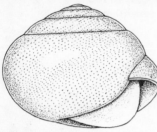

Figure 344. *Stenotrema brevipila* (Clapp).

WIDTH: 7-9 mm. RANGE: Georgia and Alabama.

Shell with about 5 whorls; pale reddish horn-colored; imperforate; thin; sculptured with dense, fine, short hairs arranged in oblique rows. The body whorl is very convex and deeply impressed near the columellar insertion of the lip.

15a Parietal wall with a small denticle at the distal end of the parietal tooth. Fig. 345...................*Stenotrema unciferum* (Pilsbry)

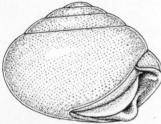

Figure 345. *Stenotrema unciferum* (Pilsbry).

WIDTH: 6.7-8.3 mm. RANGE: Arkansas.

Shell with 5-5½ whorls; dull yellow to cinnamon-buff colored; imperforate; sculptured with very fine, short, golden hairs arranged in oblique rows. The interdenticular sinus is deep and round.

15b Parietal wall without a denticle at the distal end of the parietal tooth 16

16a Shell relatively small, 6 mm. or less in diameter. Fig. 346......
....*Stenotrema pilula* (Pilsbry)

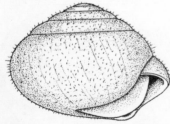

Figure 346. *Stenotrema pilula* (Pilsbry).

WIDTH: 5.7-6 mm. RANGE: North Carolina and Tennessee.

Shell with about 5 whorls; brownish-tan to cinnamon-brown; imperforate; sculptured with minute scale-like radial laminae and with periostracal hairs. The hairs are longer at the shell periphery.

16b Shell larger, more than 6 mm. in diameter.................17

17a Shell surface without periostracal hairs or papillae...........18

17b Shell surface sculptured with periostracal hairs or papillae....21

18a Shell 9 mm. or less in diameter...........................19

18b Shell larger, 9.8 mm. or more in diameter...................20

19a Spire depressed, height about ½ the diameter. Fig. 347........
..............................*Stenotrema blandianum* (Pilsbry)

WIDTH: 7.6-8.3 mm. RANGE: Missouri.

Shell with about 5 whorls; cinnamon-buff to cinnamon-brown; imperforate. The apertural structure of the shell of this species is similar to that of *S. unciferum* (Fig. 345), but the shell of that species differs by being hirsute and less depressed.

Figure 347. *Stenotrema blandianum* (Pilsbry).

19b Spire raised, height more than 2/3 the diameter. Fig. 348........
...........................*Stenotrema magnifumosum* (Pilsbry)

WIDTH: 6.4-9 mm. RANGE: North Carolina, Georgia and Tennessee.

Shell with 5-5½ whorls; wood-brown to cinnamon-brown; imperforate. The shell of this species is similar to *S. edvardsi* (see Fig. 336), but the apertural characters are more strongly developed and the periphery is more bluntly angular. It is usually smaller than *S. altispira* (see Fig. 361).

Figure 348. *Stenotrema magnifumosum* (Pilsbry).

20a Shell depressed. Fig. 349.....................................
.....................*Stenotrema stenotrema* form *nudum* Pilsbry

WIDTH: 9.8-10.8 mm. RANGE: Tennessee and Alabama.

Shell with 5-6 whorls; brownish-tan to cinnamon-brown. The shell of this form is very similar to *S. stenotrema s. s.* (see Fig. 358), but is totally without hairs and the portion of the parietal tooth between the basal lip notch and interdenticular sinus is higher and shorter.

Figure 349. *Stenotrema stenotrema* form *nudum* Pilsbry.

20b Shell globose. Fig. 350...........*Stenotrema depilatum* (Pilsbry)

Figure 350. *Stenotrema depilatum* (Pilsbry).

WIDTH: 10.2-11 mm. RANGE: North Carolina and Tennessee.

Shell with 5½-6 whorls; tawny-olive to pale brown imperforate; thin; sculptured with rather coarse, unevenly spaced radial striae and fine spiral striae. The apertural characters are similar to S. *altispira* (see Fig. 361), but the aperture is wider and the basal notch smaller.

21a Notch in basal lip very small and shallow, not well developed. Fig. 351, a.....22

21b Notch in basal lip narrow, but rather well developed. Fig. 351, b..............23

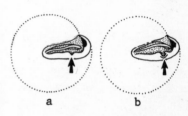

Fig. 351. a, Basal lip notch shallow; b, basal lip notch deep.

22a Shell 11.8 mm. or more in diameter. Fig. 352.....................
.....................................*Stenotrema florida* Pilsbry

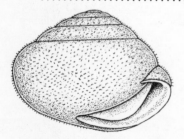

Figure 352. *Stenotrema florida* Pilsbry.

WIDTH: 11.8-12.5 mm. RANGE: Florida.

Shell with 5½-6 whorls; olive-tan; imperforate; densely sculptured with short hairs. The parietal tooth is long and slender and curves inward. Its distal end hooks rather abruptly inward.

22b Shell less than 9 mm. in diameter. Fig. 353....................
..................................Stenotrema waldense Archer

WIDTH: 8 mm. RANGE: Tennessee.

Shell with about 5 whorls; light chestnut-brown; d u l l; imperforate; rather solid. The body whorl is slightly angular at the periphery. The shell of this species is similar to S. *edvardsi* (see Fig. 336), but has a shorter parietal lamella and a more rounded periphery.

Figure 353. *Stenotrema waldense* Archer.

23a Interdenticular sinus deep. Fig. 354, a 24

23b Interdenticular sinus shallow. Fig. 354, b 25

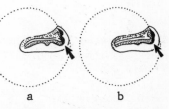

a   b

Fig. 354. a, Interdenticular sinus deep; b, interdenticular sinus shallow.

24a Shell 7 mm. or less in diameter. Fig. 355......................
..................................Stenotrema deceptum (Clapp)

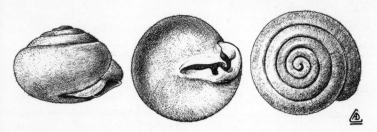

Figure 355. *Stenotrema deceptum* (Clapp).

WIDTH: 6.2-7 mm. RANGE: Tennessee and Alabama.

Shell with 5½-6 whorls; cinnamon buff-colored; imperforate; sculptured with very fine, close, short hairs. The distal end of the parietal tooth curves into the interdenticular sinus.

145

24b Shell larger, 7.6 mm. or more in diameter. Fig. 356.............
.....................................*Stenotrema exodon* (Pilsbry)

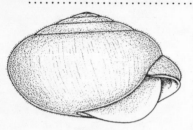

Figure 356. *Stenotrema exodon* (Pilsbry).

WIDTH: 7.6-10.5 mm. RANGE: Georgia, Tennessee and Alabama.

Shell with 5½-6 whorls; pale olive-buff to cinnamon-buff; imperforate; sculptured with close, short hairs or papillae. The shell is similar to *S. stenotrema* (Fig. 358), but is more depressed.

25a Aperture narrow (Fig. 357, a)
.........................26

25b Aperture wider (Fig. 357, b)
.........................27

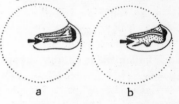

Fig. 357. a, Aperture narrow; b, aperture wide.

26a Shell depressed. Fig. 358........*Stenotrema stenotrema* (Pfeiffer)

Figure 358. *Stenotrema stenotrema* (Pfeiffer).

WIDTH: 7.8-12.8 mm. RANGE: Virginia to Georgia, west to Ohio, Missouri, Oklahoma and Louisiana.

Shell with 5-6 whorls; brownish-tan to cinnamon-brown; imperforate; sculptured with uneven radial striae and rather short hairs. The shell of this species is similar to *S. hirsutum* (Fig. 360), but has a narrower aperture and a wider basal lip.

26b Shell subglobose. Fig. 359....*Stenotrema magnifumosum* (Pilsbry)

Figure 359. *Stenotrema magnifumosum* (Pilsbry).

WIDTH: 6.4-9 mm. RANGE: North Carolina, Georgia and Tennessee.

Shell with 5-5½ whorls; wood-brown to cinnamon-brown; imperforate. The shell of this species is similar to *S. edvardsi* (see Fig. 336), but the apertural characters are more strongly developed and the periphery is more bluntly angular. It is usually smaller than *S. altispira* (Fig. 361).

146

27a Shell depressed. Fig. 360............*Stenotrema hirsutum* (Say)

WIDTH: 6.2-11 mm. RANGE: Massachusetts to Georgia, west to Minnesota, Kansas and Mississippi.

Shell with 5-5½ whorls; cinnamon-buff to tan; sculptured with oblique rows of rather stiff hairs. The subspecies *S. hirsutum barbatum* has larger, stiffer, more widely spaced hairs.

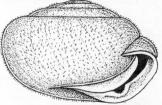

Figure 360. *Stenotrema hirsutum* (Say).

27b Shell globose. Fig. 361............*Stenotrema altispira* (Pilsbry)

WIDTH: 8.4-11.2 mm. RANGE: North Carolina and Tennessee.

Shell with 5½-6½ whorls; tawny-olive to pale brown. The shell of this species is similar to *S. depilatum* (see Fig. 350), but is sculptured with periostracal hairs. It differs from *S. magnifumosum* (see Fig. 348) by its distinct hirsuteness of the upper surface.

Figure 361. *Stenotrema altispira* (Pilsbry).

28a Aperture relatively small in relation to overall size of shell (Figs. 362, a, b, c), or aperture nearly closed by teeth or with the parietal callus often biramose and having a raised proximal edge (Figs. 364, a, c). Genera *Polygyriscus, Polygyra*.....................29

28b Aperture usually relatively large, parietal callus not biramose and without a raised proximal edge (Figs. 362, d, e). Genera *Mesodon* (in part), *Triodopsis* (in part)................................51

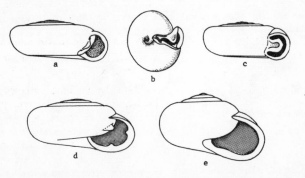

Fig. 362. a, Shell with relatively small aperture; b, shell aperture nearly closed with teeth; c, shell with biramose parietal tooth; d, e, shells with relatively large apertures.

29a Shell small, 4.5 mm. or less in diameter; aperture and last part of body whorl prominently deflected basally. Fig. 363..........
................................*Polygyriscus virginianus* (Burch)

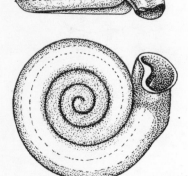

WIDTH: 3.9-4.4 mm. RANGE: Virginia.

Shell with 4-5 whorls; wood brown; discoidal; sculptured with papillate spiral lines. This peculiar snail is probably not related to other polygyrids, but is temporarily left with the Polygyridae.

Figure 363. *Polygyriscus virginianus* (Burch).

29b Shell larger, usually more than 4.5 mm. in diameter, or if smaller, without prominently deflected aperture. Genus *Polygyra*......30

30a Apertural lip without teeth. Subgenus *Polygyra*...............31

30b Apertural lip with two or three teeth (Fig. 364, a). Subgenus *Daedalochila* 32

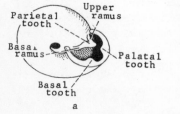

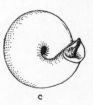

Fig. 364. a, Apertural terminology in *Polygyra*; b, U-shaped parietal tooth; c, raised proximal edge of parietal callus.

31a Shell with a parietal lamella ending within the first half of the last whorl. Fig. 365..................*Polygyra cereolus* (Muhlfeld)

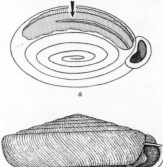

WIDTH: 6-18.2 mm. RANGE: Florida.

Shell with 5½-9 whorls; uniformly wood brown to white with radial streaks of pale brown; discoidal or with a raised spire; sculptured with rib-striae. The periphery is angular to subcarinate.

Figure 365. *Polygyra cereolus* (Muhl-feld).

31b Shell without a parietal lamella in the first half of the last whorl. Fig. 366............................*Polygyra septemvolva* Say

WIDTH: 7-15.6 mm. RANGE: Georgia and Florida, west to Texas.

Shell with 6-10 whorls; cinnamon-buff to reddish-horn or lighter. The shell of this species is very similar to *P. cereolus* (Fig. 365), differing mainly by the lack of an internal lamina. It also usually has a more solid shell with a less acutely angled periphery.

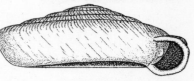

Figure 366. *Polygyra septemvolva* Say.

32a Proximal edge of parietal callus conspicuously raised (Fig. 364, c) **33**
32b Proximal edge of parietal callus not raised...................**37**
33a Parietal tooth U-shaped, extending deeply into the aperture. Figs. 364, b; 367........................*Polygyra hippocrepis* (Pfeiffer)

WIDTH: 11-12 mm. RANGE: Texas.

Shell with 4½-5 whorls; light brown; rather glossy; sculptured with fine rib-striae. The aperture lip is continuous and nearly triangular when viewed from below.

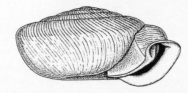

Figure 367. *Polygyra hippocrepis* (Pfeiffer).

33b Parietal tooth irregular, not U-shaped, not extending deeply into the aperture 34

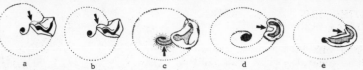

Fig. 368. a, Proximal end of the parietal callus closely appressed to the whorl; b, proximal end of the parietal callus raised and continuous; c, body whorl with a furrow parallel to the umbilical suture; d, parietal tooth triangular or square in shape; e, parietal tooth V-shaped.

34a Proximal end of the parietal callus closely appressed to the whorl. Figs. 368, a; 369 .... *Polygyra uvulifera* (Shuttleworth)

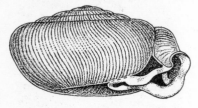

Figure 369. *Polygyra uvulifera* (Shuttleworth).

WIDTH: 11-16.4 mm. RANGE: Florida.

Shell with 5½-6½ whorls; pale brown, buff, or grayish-white; rather glossy, nearly smooth. In side view the proximal end of the parietal callus forms a sigmoid curve to the base of the body whorl.

34b Proximal end of the parietal callus raised and continuous (Fig. 368, b) 35

35a Inner part of body whorl with a furrow parallel to the umbilical suture (Fig. 368, c) 36

35b Inner part of body whorl without a furrow parallel to the umbilical suture. Fig. 370 .... *Polygyra avara* Say

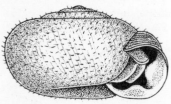

Figure 370. *Polygyra avara* Say.

WIDTH: 5.4-7.2 mm. RANGE: Florida.

Shell with 4½-5 whorls; pale cinnamon-colored; sculptured with faint growth wrinkles, miscroscopic transverse striae and close, short hairs arranged in forwardly descending rows.

36a Parietal tooth long and irregular in shape. Fig. 371.............
.......................................Polygyra auriculata Say

WIDTH: 10.9-17 mm. RANGE:
Florida.

Shell with 5½-6 whorls; cream-
buff to pale olive-buff. The shell
of *P. auriculata* is very similar to
that of *P. uvulifera* (Fig. 369), but
in the latter the lip runs forward
from the basal tooth, and its front
edge has a deep, rather narrow
sinus (Pilsbry).

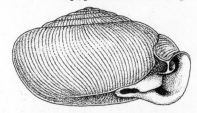

Figure 371. *Polygyra auriculata* Say.

36b Parietal tooth shorter, more or less V-shaped. Fig. 372.........
....................................Polygyra auriformis (Bland)

WIDTH: 6.7-11.5 mm. RANGE:
Georgia and Florida, west to
Texas.

Shell with 5½-6 whorls; white,
brown or horn-colored; thin; sculptured with rib-striae and microscopic spiral lines. The base of
the shell is almost smooth.

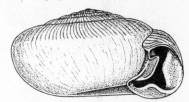

Figure 372. *Polygyra auriformis*
(Bland).

37a Parietal tooth triangular or rather square in shape (Fig. 368, d)
...38

37b Parietal tooth V-shaped (Fig. 368, e).........................43

38a Basal branch of parietal tooth without an angle (Fig. 373, a)....39

38b Basal branch of parietal tooth with an angle (Fig. 373, b)......40

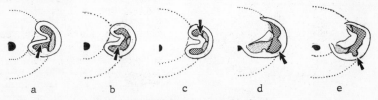

a   b   c   d   e

Fig. 373. a, Basal branch of parietal tooth without an angle; b, basal branch
of parietal tooth with an angle; c, upper branch of parietal tooth with a
projection; d, basal and palatal teeth widely separated; e, basal and
palatal teeth narrowly separated.

39a Base of shell smooth; umbilicus small. Fig. 374.................
.....................................*Polygyra jacksoni* (Bland)
WIDTH: 7-9.3 mm. RANGE: Missouri, Arkansas and Oklahoma.

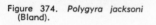

Shell with 5½-6 whorls; pale or dark horn-colored. The shell of this species is somewhat similar to that of *P. plicata* (Fig. 378), but differs from that species by its smaller umbilicus (1/5-1/4 the shell diameter) and weaker sculpture.

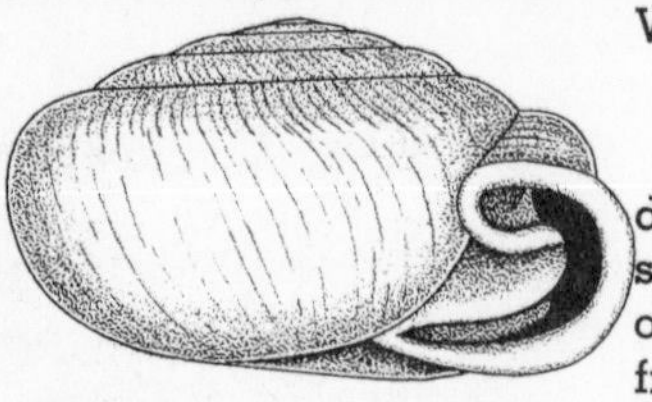

Figure 374. *Polygyra jacksoni* (Bland).

39b Base of shell rib-striate; umbilicus larger. Fig. 375...............
.....................................*Polygyra peregrina* Rehder
WIDTH: 8-8.4 mm. RANGE: Arkansas.

Shell with 6-6½ whorls; pale corneous, somewhat glossy. The shell of this species is similar to both *P. troostiana* (Fig. 377) and *P. plicata* (Fig. 378), but differs by its narrower parietal tooth.

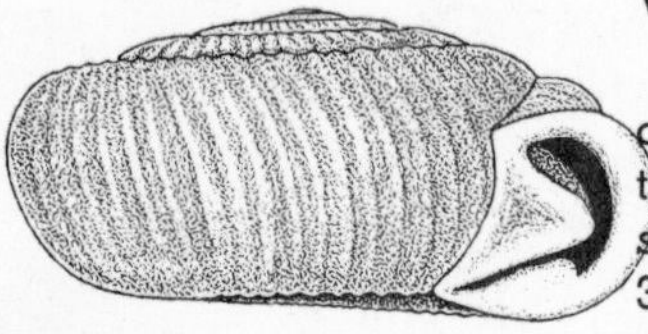

Figure 375. *Polygyra peregrina* Rehder.

40a Basal tooth smaller than palatal tooth.........................41
40b Basal tooth and palatal tooth nearly equal in size..............42
41a Shell periphery carinate or strongly angular. Fig. 376..........
.....................................*Polygyra fatigiata* Say
WIDTH: 8-10.4 mm. RANGE: Indiana, Kentucky and Tennessee.

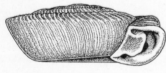

Shell with about 6 whorls; pale cinnamon-buff; sculptured with spiral striae, irregular microscopic growth wrinkles and radial rib-striae. The aperture is like that of *P. troostiana* (Fig. 377).

Figure 376. *Polygyra fatigiata* Say.

41b Shell periphery only bluntly angular. Fig. 377..................
.....................................*Polygyra troostiana* Lea
WIDTH: 6.7-8.1 mm. RANGE: Tennessee and Alabama.

Shell with 5-6 whorls, tannish-brown. The shell of this species is usually smaller and less depressed than *P. fatigiata* (Fig. 376). It differs from *P. plicata* (Fig. 378) by having the rib-striae extend to the apertural lip.

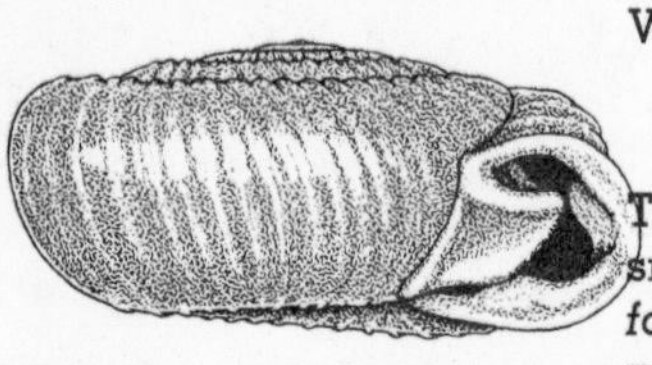

Figure 377. *Polygyra troostiana* Lea.

42a Upper branch of parietal tooth with a small projection. Figs. 373, c; 378.....................................*Polygyra plicata* Say

WIDTH: 5.5-7.7 mm. RANGE: Indiana to Alabama and Georgia.

Shell with about 5 whorls; tannish-brown. This species resembles *P. jacksoni* (see Fig. 374) in having a small, smooth, convex area behind the outer lip, but differs in the wide umbilicus and the sculpture (Pilsbry).

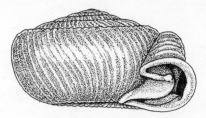

Figure 378. *Polygyra plicata* Say.

42b Upper branch of parietal tooth without a projection. Fig. 379....
....*Polygyra dorfeuilliana* Lea

WIDTH: 6.7-9.7 mm. RANGE: Illinois to Louisiana and Texas.

Shell with about 5½ whorls; pale tan-brown; sculptured with coarse, weak ribs. The shell of this species is very similar to *P. troostiana* (Fig. 377), but the rib-striae are not as strong.

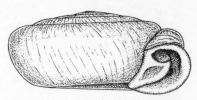

Figure 379. *Polygyra dorfeuilliana* Lea.

43a Shell sculptured with fine periostracal hairs..................**44**

43b Shell without fine periostracal hairs..........................**46**

44a Shell small, 4.7 mm. or less in diameter. Fig. 380...............
.....................................*Polygyra pustula* (Férussac)

WIDTH: 4-4.7 mm. RANGE: South Carolina, Georgia, Florida and Alabama.

Shell with about 4½ whorls; pale cinnamon-buff. The shell of this species is similar to *P. leporina* (Fig. 381) and *P. pustuloides* (Fig. 382), but has a deep spiral groove around the umbilicus and weaker growth wrinkles.

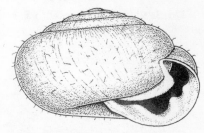

Figure 380. *Polygyra pustula* (Férussac).

44b Shell larger, 5 mm. or more in diameter........................**45**

45a Umbilicus partially or nearly covered by basal lip. Fig. 381.....
.... *Polygyra leporina* (Gould)

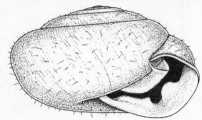

Figure 381. *Polygyra leporina* (Gould).

WIDTH: 5-6.5 mm. RANGE: Indiana to Alabama, west to Missouri and Texas.

Shell with 4½-5 whorls; pale brown to olive-buff; depressed; sculptured with delicate hairs on rather sparse papillae. The basal tooth is situated on a strong ridge.

45b Umbilicus not partially covered by basal lip. Fig. 382...........
.... *Polygyra pustuloides* (Bland)

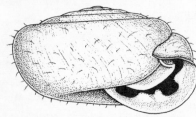

Figure 382. *Polygyra pustuloides* (Bland).

WIDTH: 5-5.5 mm. RANGE: South Carolina to Florida, west to Tennessee and Mississippi.

Shell with 4-5 whorls; orange-buff to pale horn-colored; depressed; umbilicate; sculptured with delicate striae and fine, sparse hairs.

46a Inner part of body whorl with a furrow parallel to the umbilical suture (Fig. 368, c)...47

46b Inner part of body whorl without a furrow parallel to the umbilical suture 48

47a Shell relatively small, 8.8 mm. or less in diameter. Fig. 383.....
.... *Polygyra mooreana* (Binney)

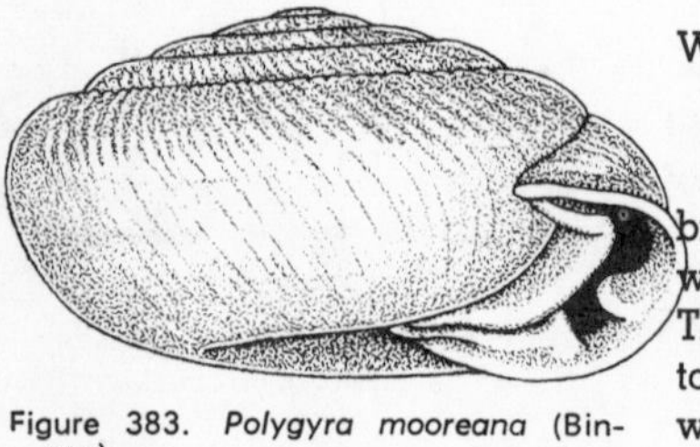

Figure 383. *Polygyra mooreana* (Binney).

WIDTH: 6.5-8.8 mm. RANGE: Texas.

Shell with 5-6 whorls; pale brown; upper surface sculptured with rib-striae, the base smooth. The shell of this species is similar to *P. texasiana* (Fig. 388), but the whorls increase more slowly.

47b Shell larger, 9 mm. or more in diameter. Fig. 384..............
....*Polygyra tholus* (Binney)

WIDTH: 9-11.2 mm. RANGE:
Texas.

Shell with 6-7½ whorls; pale
brown. The shell of this species
is very similar to *P. mooreana*
(Fig. 383), but is larger and has
a relatively wider umbilicus.

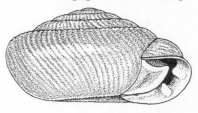

Figure 384. *Polygyra tholus* (Binney)

48a Basal and palatal teeth widely separated. (See Fig. 373, d). Fig.
385..............................*Polygyra triodontoides* (Bland)

WIDTH: 8.7-10 mm. RANGE:
Missouri to Louisiana; Oklahoma and Texas.

Shell with about 5 whorls;
pale horn-colored; thin; sculptured with rather poorly developed rib-striae above, the base
smooth. The last whorl is more
strongly ribbed near the aperture.

Figure 385. *Polygyra triodontoides* (Bland)

48b Basal and palatal teeth separated by only a narrow gap (see Fig.
373, e)..49

49a Body whorl without coarser transverse striae behind the lip. Fig.
386..................................*Polygyra latispira* Pilsbry

WIDTH: 11.8-12 mm. RANGE:
Texas.

Shell with 5½-6 whorls; buff or
pale yellow. The shell of this species is similar to that of *P. chisosensis* (Fig. 387) and *P. texasiana*
(Fig. 388), but is more closely
coiled and has finer, more even
striae.

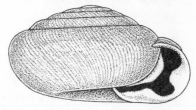

Figure 386. *Polygyra latispira* Pilsbry

49b Body whorl with coarser transverse striae behind the lip........50

50a **Basal branch of parietal tooth much larger than the upper branch. Fig. 387**.............................*Polygyra chisosensis* **Pilsbry**

WIDTH: 9.5-14.2 mm. RANGE: Texas.

Figure 387. *Polygyra chisosensis* Pilsbry

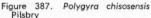

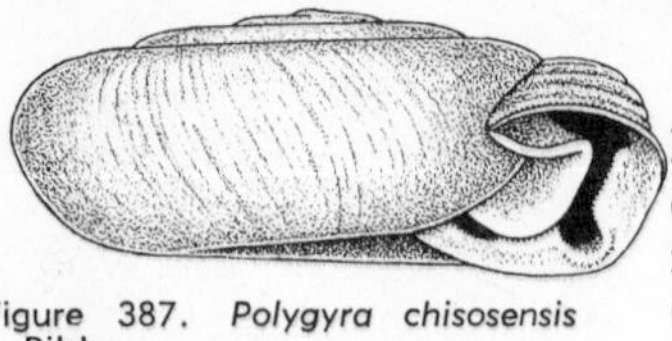

Shell with about 5 whorls; pale brown, glossy, slightly translucent; depressed. The shell of this species is very similar to that of *P. texasiana* (Fig. 388), but has weaker sculpture.

50b **Basal and upper branches of parietal tooth nearly equal in size. Fig. 388**..........................*Polygyra texasiana* **(Moricand)**

WIDTH: 6.5-13.7 mm. RANGE: Arkansas and Louisiana, west to New Mexico.

Figure 388. *Polygyra texasiana* (Moricand)

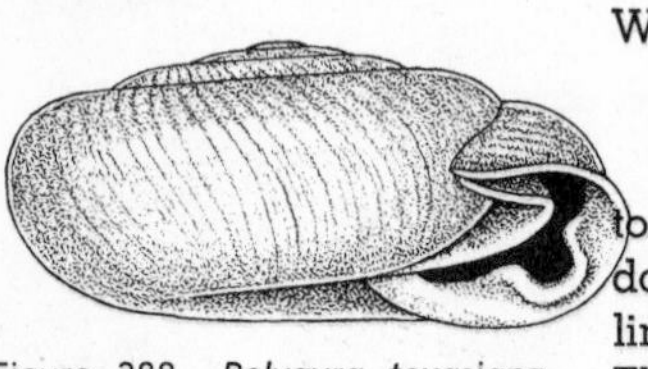

Shell with 4½-5½ whorls; light brown to pale buff, sometimes with a faintly darker band; sculptured with fine growth lines, and rib-striae on the upper surface. The base is rather smooth, only weakly striate.

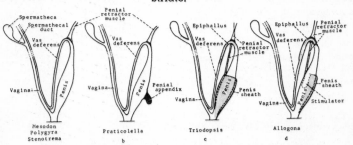

Fig. 389. Diagnostic features of the reproductive systems of the Polygyridae. The polygyrid genera are distinguished mainly by characters of the reproductive organs. While the shells of *Polygyra* and *Stenotrema* are distinctly characteristic for their respective groups, the shells of the other genera do not so readily fall into morphological types. Similar shell forms often occur throughout *Allogona, Mesodon, Praticolella* and *Triodopsis.*

51a **Shell imperforate (without an umbilical opening)**..............**52**
51b **Shell perforate or umbilicate**..................................**75**
52a **Shell with a tooth (palatal) on the outer apertural lip**..........**53**
52b **Shell without a tooth on the outer apertural lip**................**60**
53a **Palatal tooth situated in center and most distal part of the outer lip; shell usually less than 17 mm. in diameter**...............**54**
53b **Palatal tooth situated in the upper part of the outer lip; shell usually more than 17 mm. in diameter**..............................**57**
54a **Basal tooth well developed**.....................................**55**
54b **Basal tooth not well developed**.................................**56**

55a Palatal tooth rather deeply recessed. Fig. 390.................
.................................*Mesodon rugeli* **(Shuttleworth)**

WIDTH: 7.8-16.4 mm. RANGE: Virginia to Georgia, west to Kentucky and Alabama.

Shell with about 5½ whorls; waxy horn-colored; sculptured with low bristles which appear as scales when their points are broken off. The shell is imperforate, the aperture depressed.

Figure 390. *Mesodon rugeli* (Shuttleworth)

55b Palatal tooth only slightly recessed. Fig. 391.................
......................................*Mesodon inflectus* **(Say)**

WIDTH: 7.5-13.8 mm. RANGE: North Carolina to Florida, west to Michigan, Oklahoma and Louisiana.

Shell with 4½-5½ whorls; cream buff-colored to light yellowish-horn; sculptured with short periostracal processes and fine radiating striae and wrinkles.

Figure 391. *Mesodon inflectus* (Say)

56a Palatal tooth relatively large. Fig. 392....*Mesodon smithi* **(Clapp)**

WIDTH: 13.5-18.5 mm. RANGE: Alabama.

Shell with about 5½ whorls; horn-colored; densely sculptured with scaly epidermal processes and hairs, and weak growth wrinkles. The basal lamella is long and low.

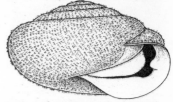

Figure 392. *Mesodon smithi* (Clapp)

56b Palatal tooth relatively small. Fig. 393........................
....................*Mesodon magazinensis* **(Pilsbry and Ferriss)**

WIDTH: 11.4-14.3 mm. RANGE: Arkansas.

Shell with 4½-5 whorls; cream buff-colored to light yellowish-horn. The shell of this species is very similar to *M. inflectus* (Fig. 391), but is more abruptly contracted behind the lip.

Figure 393. *Mesodon magazinensis* (Pilsbry and Ferriss)

57a Shell sculptured with short stiff hairs. Fig. 394.................
..................................*Triodopsis denotata* (Férussac)

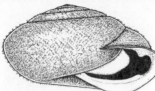

Figure 394. *Triodopsis denotata* (Férussac)

WIDTH: 19-25.6 mm. RANGE: Vermont to North Carolina, west to Michigan and Mississippi.

Shell with about 5½ whorls; tawny olive to snuff brown; sculptured with rather weak, coarse, radiating striae, fine wrinkles and close-set periostracal processes or hairs.

57b Shell without hairs...58

58a Shell periphery carinate. Fig. 395......*Triodopsis obstricta* (Say)

Figure 395. *Triodopsis obstricta* (Say)

WIDTH: 17-26.6 mm. RANGE: South Carolina, west to Illinois and Arkansas.

Shell with about 5½ whorls; pale brown; usually imperforate, but sometimes with a slight perforation; sculptured with transverse rib-striae, weak spiral striae, and fine wrinkles.

58b Shell periphery angular or rounded..........................59

59a Shell periphery distinctly angular. Fig. 396.....................
..................................*Triodopsis caroliniensis* (Lea)

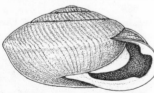

Figure 396. *Triodopsis caroliniensis* (Lea)

WIDTH: 19.2-23.1 mm. RANGE: South Carolina and Georgia, west to Tennessee and Louisiana.

Shell with about 5 whorls; tawny olive to cinnamon; sculptured with rib-striae and minute wrinkles. The shell is depressed and imperforate; its aperture is tri-lobed.

59b Shell periphery rounded or only very bluntly angular . Fig. 397...
.....................................*Triodopsis fosteri* (Baker)

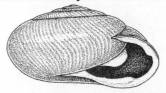

WIDTH: 8-25 mm. RANGE: New Jersey; Indiana to Iowa, south to Mississippi and Louisiana.

Shell with about 4½ whorls; cinnamon-buff to brownish-horn. The shell of this species is very similar to *Mesodon appressus* (see Fig. 405), but the sculpture is coarser and the parietal tooth is larger and heavier.

Figure 397. *Triodopsis fosteri* (Baker)

60a Shell globose to subglobose...................................**61**

60b Shell depressed **66**

61a Shell marked with reddish-brown color bands. Fig. 398..........
.....................................*Triodopsis multilineata* (Say)

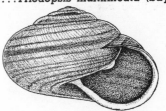

WIDTH: 14.5-32 mm. RANGE: Ohio to Mississippi, west to Minnesota, Nebraska and Arkansas.

Shell with 5½-6 whorls; ivory yellow to olive buff, with dark reddish-brown bands; rather glossy. Sculptured with transverse striae and weak spiral lines.

Figure 398. *Triodopsis multilineata* (Say)

61b Shell without color bands....................................**62**
62a Shell large, 19 mm. or more in diameter......................**63**
62b Shell smaller, less than 19 mm. in diameter..................**64**
63a Basal lip with a long lamina along the inner edge. Fig. 399......
.....................................*Mesodon elevatus* (Say)

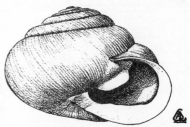

WIDTH: 19.8-26.3 mm. RANGE: New York to South Carolina, west to Michigan, Arkansas and Mississippi.

Shell with 6-7 whorls; pale yellow to light olive; sculptured with fine transverse striae, close spiral lines, and often with scattered malleations.

Figure 399. *Mesodon elevatus* (Say)

63b Basal lip with a blunt tooth near the columellar insertion. Fig. 400.
....................................*Mesodon zaletus* (Binney)

Figure 400. *Mesodon zaletus* (Binney)

WIDTH: 19-31 mm. RANGE: New York to North Carolina, west to Wisconsin, Iowa and Oklahoma.

Shell with 5½-6 whorls; cream-colored to cinnamon-buff; sculptured with fine oblique striae and microscopic spiral lines. The parietal wall usually has an oblique white tooth, but occasionally it is lacking.

64a Shell sculptured with fine, but well-developed spiral striae or indented lines. Fig. 401......................*Mesodon clarki* (Lea)

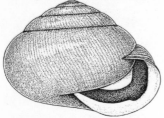

Figure 401. *Mesodon clarki* (Lea)

WIDTH: 13-18.2 mm. RANGE: North Carolina, Georgia and Tennessee.

Shell with 5½-6½ whorls; pale buff to tan; sculptured with rib-striae and fine spiral lines. This species is similar to *M. elevatus* (Fig. 399), but is smaller.

64b Shell without, or with nearly obsolete, spiral indented lines.....65

65a Shell somewhat depressed; parietal tooth strongly developed. Fig. 402....................................*Mesodon archeri* Pilsbry

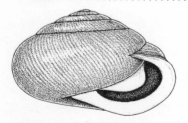

Figure 402. *Mesodon archeri* Pilsbry

WIDTH: 13.7-14.6 mm. RANGE: Tennessee.

Shell with about 5½ whorls; tannish-brown to dark brown. The shell of this species is similar to *M. clarki* (Fig. 401), but is more depressed and has stronger rib-striae.

65b Shell less depressed; parietal tooth less strongly developed. Fig. 403................................*Mesodon wheatleyi* (Bland)

WIDTH: 13.2-16.4 mm. RANGE: North Carolina to Georgia, west to Tennessee and Alabama.

Shell with about 5½ whorls; reddish horn-colored; sculptured with rib-striae and minute granulations, which may bear short, fine hairs. Some specimens may be found that lack a parietal tooth.

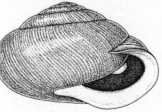

Figure 403. *Mesodon wheatleyi* (Bland)

66a Shell relatively small, 10 mm. or less in diameter. Fig. 404......
....*Mesodon christyi* (Bland)

WIDTH: 8.3-10 mm. RANGE: North Carolina, South Carolina, Tennessee and Alabama.

Shell with about 4½ whorls; dark horn-colored; sculptured with transverse rib-striae, but lacking spiral striae or indented lines. The parietal tooth is relatively long.

Figure 404. *Mesodon christyi* (Bland)

66b Shell larger, more than 12 mm. in diameter....................67
67a Shell with spiral sculpture....................................68
67b Shell without spiral sculpture...............................73
68a Spiral sculpturing of body whorl consisting of minute papillae..69
68b Spiral sculpturing of body whorl consisting of incised lines.....70
69a Shell 20 mm. or less in diameter. Fig. 405....................
....*Mesodon appressus* (Say)

WIDTH: 13-19.5 mm. RANGE: Ohio and Indiana to Alabama; Virginia.

Shell with 4½-5 whorls; cinnamon-buff to brownish-horn; somewhat glossy. The shell is rather strongly depressed, with a distinctly angular body whorl.

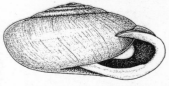

Figure 405. *Mesodon appressus* (Say)

69b Shell 22 mm. or more in diameter. Fig. 406......................
....................*Mesodon sargentianus* (Johnson and Pilsbry)

Figure 406. *Mesodon sargentianus* (Johnson and Pilsbry)

WIDTH: 22.3-26.8 mm. RANGE: Alabama.

Shell with about 6 whorls; pale cinnamon-buff to tan; somewhat glossy; imperforate; rather strongly depressed. The body whorl is strongly angular.

70a Shell surface glossy...71

70b Shell surface dull. Fig. 407..........*Triodopsis dentifera* (Binney)

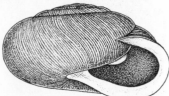

Figure 407. *Triodopsis dentifera* (Binney)

WIDTH: 20-30.5 mm. RANGE: Maine to South Carolina.

Shell with 5-5½ whorls; pale olive; sculptured with transverse rib-striae and wrinkles, and spiral incised lines. The shell of this species is similar to *T. albolabris* (see Fig. 441), but is thinner, much more depressed, and has a tooth.

71a Basal lip of aperture thickened by a basal lamina. Fig. 408......
....................................*Mesodon perigraptus* Pilsbry

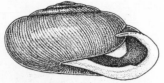

Figure 408. *Mesodon perigraptus* Pilsbry

WIDTH: 15.8-23.4 mm. RANGE: North Carolina to Florida, west to Tennessee and Arkansas.

Shell with 5½-6 whorls; tan-colored, glossy; depressed; sculptured with rather fine, close, transverse striae and incised spiral lines. The basal tooth is blade-like and distally truncate.

71b Basal lip of aperture without a distinct basal lamina...........72

72a Shell yellowish-olive. Fig. 409.........*Mesodon ferrissi* (Pilsbry)

WIDTH: 19.6-23.3 mm. RANGE: North Carolina and Tennessee.

Shell with 4½-5½ whorls; pale yellowish-olive to tannish-o l i v e. The shell of this species is similar to *Triodopsis dentifera* (Fig. 407), but has a more glossy surface and papillose early whorls.

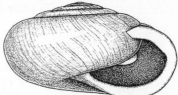

Figure 409. *Mesodon ferrissi* (Pilsbry)

72b Shell pale flesh-colored. Fig. 410.......*Mesodon roemeri* (Pfeiffer)

WIDTH: 18-24 mm. RANGE: Texas.

Shell with 4½-5 whorls; cinnamon-buff to tan; usually narrowly umbilicate or perforate, but sometimes imperforate. Sometimes a parietal tooth is present, but it is often lacking.

Figure 410. *Mesodon roemeri* (Pfeiffer)

73a Shell less than 17 mm. in diameter............................74

**73b Shell more than 17 mm. in diameter. Fig. 411................;...
.....................................*Mesodon wetherbyi* (Bland)**

WIDTH: 17.5-18.3 mm. RANGE: Kentucky and Tennessee.

Shell with 5-6 whorls; dull cinnamon-buff; sculptured with oblique, prostrate hairs. The shell of this species is very similar to *Triodopsis dentifera* (Fig. 407), but differs in sculpture.

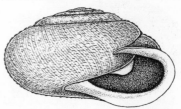

Figure 411. *Mesodon wetherbyi* (Bland)

74a Shell 12.8-13.5 mm. in diameter; light chestnut-colored. Fig. 412...
.................................*Mesodon jonesianus* (Archer)

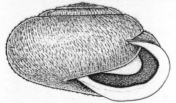

Figure 412. *Mesodon jonesianus* (Archer)

WIDTH: 12.8-13.5 mm. RANGE: Tennessee.

Shell with 5-5½ whorls; light chestnut-colored. The shell of this species is similar to *M. wetherbyi* (Fig. 411) and *M. subpalliatus* (Fig. 413), but is smaller, with a narrower last whorl.

74b Shell 13.4-16.4 mm. in diameter; buff to pale yellow-colored. Fig. 413..............................*Mesodon subpalliatus* (Pilsbry)

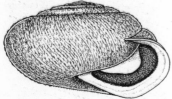

Figure 413. *Mesodon subpalliatus* (Pilsbry)

WIDTH: 13.4-16.4 mm. RANGE: North Carolina and Tennessee.

Shell with 4½-5 whorls; pale yellow to buff. The transverse striae are interrupted and in the form of low, oblong granules, which bear either erect or adnate periostracal processes, sometimes)-shaped.

75a Shell with a tooth (palatal) on the outer apertural lip.........76

75b Shell without a tooth on the outer apertural lip.................85

76a Shell relatively small, 9 mm. or less in diameter. Fig. 414.......
....*Triodopsis cragini* Call

Figure 414. *Triodopsis cragini* Call

WIDTH: 7.6-9 mm. RANGE: Missouri to Louisiana, west to Kansas and Texas.

Shell with 4½-5 whorls; reddish horn-colored, rather glossy; sculptured with prominent rib-striae. The shell of this species is similar to *T. vultuosa* (Fig. 418), but is smaller and without a distinct ridge or flange on the face of the basal lip.

76b Shell larger, more than 9 mm. in diameter...................77

77a Basal tooth in form of a long, marginal lamina. Fig. 415........
................................*Triodopsis denotata* (Férussac)

WIDTH: 19-25.6 mm. RANGE: Vermont to North Carolina, west to Michigan and Mississippi.

Shell with about 5½ whorls; tawny-olive to snuff-brown; sculptured with rather weak, coarse, radiating striae, fine wrinkles and close-set periostracal processes or hairs.

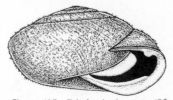

Figure 415. *Triodopsis denotata* (Férussac)

77b Basal tooth tubercular..**78**

78a Palatal tooth recessed, not marginal to the outer lip..........**79**

78b Palatal tooth not recessed, but marginal to the outer lip.......**83**

79a Umbilicus relatively wide, 1/6 to 1/4 the shell diameter......**80**

79b Umbilicus narrower, less than 1/6 the shell diameter..........**81**

80a Shell less than 13 mm. in diameter. Fig. 416...................
................................*Triodopsis neglecta* (Pilsbry)

WIDTH: 9.8-12.7 mm. RANGE: Missouri, Arkansas, Kansas and Oklahoma.

Shell with about 5½ whorls; pale olive; somewhat glossy; rather strongly depressed; sculptured with regularly spaced ribstriae. Aperture lip rather thick, widely reflected.

Figure 416. *Triodopsis neglecta* (Pilsbry)

80b Shell larger, more than 13 mm. in diameter. Fig. 417............
................................*Triodopsis fraudulenta* (Pilsbry)

WIDTH: 13.5-19.5 mm. RANGE: New York to North Carolina, west to Michigan and Missouri.

Shell with about 6 whorls; cream-buff to cinnamon-buff. The shell of this species is very similar to *T. tridentata* (Fig. 422), but is slightly less depressed and the palatal tooth is recessed.

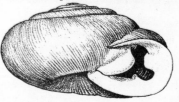

Figure 417. *Triodopsis fraudulenta* (Pilsbry)

81a Palatal tooth deeply recessed. Fig. 418........................
...................................*Triodopsis vultuosa* (Gould)

WIDTH: 9.5-14.5 mm. RANGE: Arkansas, Louisiana and Texas.

Shell with about 5½ whorls; pale tan to dark horn-colored. The shell of this species is similar to *T. fallax* (Fig. 420) and *T. vannostrandi* (Fig. 419), but the palatal tooth is more deeply recessed.

Figure 418. *Triodopsis vultuosa* (Gould)

81b Palatal tooth not deeply recessed............................82

82a Spire relatively high. Fig. 419....*Triodopsis vannostrandi* (Bland)

WIDTH: 10-13.7 mm. RANGE: South Carolina to Florida: Alabama.

Shell with 5-6½ whorls; yellowish-brown; sculptured with well-developed rib-striae. The basal and palatal teeth are usually quite blunt.

Figure 419. *Triodopsis vannostrandi* (Bland)

82b Spire more depressed. Fig. 420...........*Triodopsis fallax* (Say)

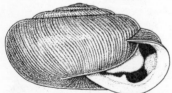

WIDTH: 9.9-13.5 mm. RANGE: New Jersey to Georgia, west to Pennsylvania and Tennessee.

Shell with about 5½ whorls; deep olive-buff to pale snuff-brown; narrowly umbilicate (umbilicus about 1/9 the shell diameter); sculptured with close, transverse striae.

Figure 420. *Triodopsis fallax* (Say)

83a Palatal tooth situated on a buttress. Fig. 421.................
.....................Triodopsis rugosa Brooks and MacMillan

WIDTH: 10.7-13.8 mm. RANGE: Virginia, West Virginia, Kentucky and Tennessee.

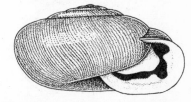

Shell with 5-5½ whorls; reddish-horn to snuff-brown; sculptured with rather prominent rib-striae and very weak spiral striae. South of West Virginia there is a more finely striate subspecies, *T. rugosa anteridon* Pilsbry.

Figure 421. *Triodopsis rugosa* Brooks and MacMillan

83b Palatal tooth not on a buttress...............................84

84a Distal end of parietal tooth directed to a point below the palatal tooth (see Fig. 422a). Fig. 422..........Triodopsis tridentata (Say)

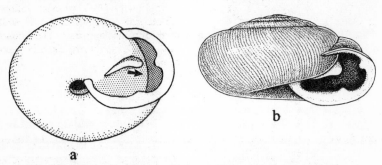

Fig. 422. *Triodopsis tridentata* (Say). a, Distal end of parietal tooth pointing below the palatal tooth.

WIDTH: 11.7-25.3 mm. RANGE: New Hampshire to Georgia, west to Michigan,, Missouri and Mississippi.

Shell with 5-6 whorls; light cream to pale cinnamon-buff; sculptured with transverse rib-striae, minute wrinkles and with minute papillae around the umbilicus. The umbilicus is about 1/7 the shell diameter.

84b Distal end of parietal tooth pointed at or above the palatal tooth (see Fig. 423, a). Fig. 423 . . . . *Triodopsis hopetonensis* (Shuttleworth)

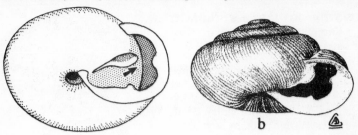

Fig. 423. *Triodopsis hopetonensis* (Shuttleworth). a, Distal end of parietal tooth pointing above the palatal tooth.

WIDTH: 9.2-13 mm. RANGE: Virginia to Florida; Alabama.

Shell with 4½-5½ whorls; olive-horn colored. The shell of this species is similar to *T. fallax* (Fig. 420), but is darker, has a thinner lip and more widely separated teeth.

85a Shell relatively small, less than 12 mm. in diameter 86

85b Shell relatively large, 15 mm. or more in diameter 89

86a Outer and basal lips merge with a gradual curve 87

86b Outer and basal lips meet at an angle 88

**87a Shell less than 7 mm. in diameter. Fig. 424 . . . .
. . . . *Praticolella lawae* (Lewis)**

Figure 424. *Praticolella lawae* (Lewis)

WIDTH: 5.7-6.1 mm. RANGE: North Carolina to Georgia, west to Tennessee and Mississippi.

Shell with 4½-5 whorls; pale cinnamon-buff; rather thin; very narrowly umbilicate; sculptured with indistinct growth wrinkles and very fine, short hairs or hair scars arranged in diagonal rows.

87b Shell more than 7 mm. in diameter. Fig. 425................
................................*Triodopsis soelneri* (Henderson)

WIDTH: 10-11 mm. RANGE: North
Carolina.

Shell with about 5½ whorls; ma-
hogany-colored, rather glossy; sculptured with rather prominent rib-striae.
The shell of this species is somewhat
like *Mesodon christyi* (see Fig. 404),
but is larger and perforate.

Figure 425. *Triodopsis soelneri*
(Henderson)

88a Shell usually 9 mm. or less in diameter. Fig. 426.............
.......................................*Stenotrema leai* (Binney)

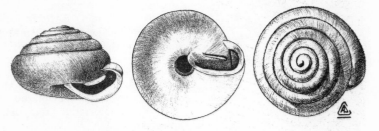

Figure 426. *Stenotrema leai* (Binney)

WIDTH: 6.1-9.4 mm. RANGE: New York to Virginia, west to South
Dakota and Texas.
Shell with 5½-6½ whorls; tannish-olive to cinnamon-buff; umbilicate; somewhat glossy. Sculptured with fine growth lines, and often
on the last whorl, with fine hairs. This species is called *Polygyra
monodon* in many older references.

88b Shell usually more than 9 mm. in diameter. Fig. 427...........
...................................*Stenotrema fraternum* (Say)

WIDTH: 7.8-11.4 mm. RANGE: New
Hampshire to Georgia, west to Minnesota and Oklahoma.

Shell with 5-6 whorls; pale tan to
tawny-olive or cinnamon-buff; imperforate or perforate. The shell of this
species differs from *S. leai* (Fig. 426)
by being more loosely coiled, having
a smaller umbilicus and a rougher
surface.

Figure 427. *Stenotrema fraternum*
(Say)

89a Umbilicus ½ covered to nearly covered by the reflected basal
lip 90

89b Umbilicus hardly covered by the reflected basal lip 91

90a Shell subglobose. Fig. 428 .... *Mesodon thyroidus* (Say)

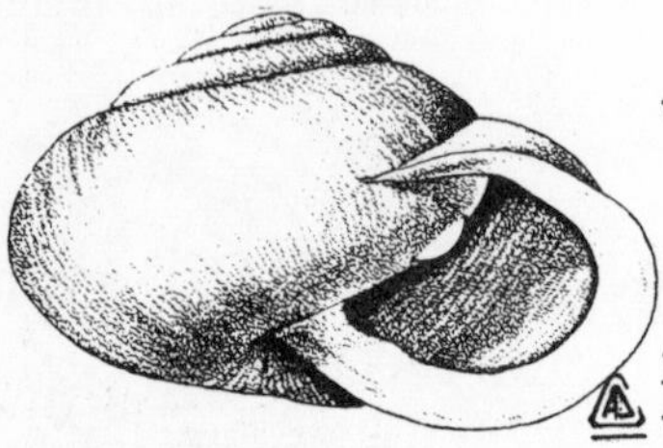

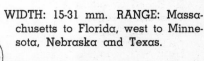

Figure 428. *Mesodon thyroidus* (Say)

WIDTH: 15-31 mm. RANGE: Massachusetts to Florida, west to Minnesota, Nebraska and Texas.

Shell with 5-5½ whorls; ivory yellow to pale yellowish-green; somewhat glossy; thin; sculptured with
fine transverse striae and minute
spiral lines.

90b Shell depressed. Fig. 429 .... *Mesodon roemeri* (Pfeiffer)

Figure 429. *Mesodon roemeri* (Pfeiffer)

WIDTH: 18-24 mm. RANGE: Texas.

Shell with 4½-5 whorls; cinnamon
buff to tan; usually narrowly umbilicate or perforate, but sometimes imperforate. Sometimes a parietal tooth
is present, but it is often lacking.

91a Shell usually less than 27 mm. in diameter; lip expansion narrow. Fig. 430............................*Mesodon sayanus* (Pilsbry)

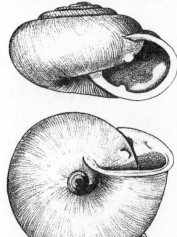

WIDTH: 19.4-27 mm. RANGE: Vermont to North Carolina, west to Michigan and Tennessee.

Shell with about 5½ whorls; pale yellow to pale olive-tan; glossy; umbilicate (umbilicus about 1/7 the shell diameter); thin; sculptured with rather fine, transverse striae and microscopic spiral lines.

Figure 430. *Mesodon sayanus* (Pilsbry)

91b Shell usually more than 27 mm. in diameter; lip expansion wide. Fig. 431.........................*Mesodon chilhoweensis* (Lewis)

WIDTH: 26.5-42 mm. RANGE: North Carolina and Tennessee.

Shell with 6-6½ whorls; cream-colored. The shell of this species differs from *M. sayanus* (Fig. 430) by its size, its more broadly reflected lip, the absence of a basal tooth, and the more distinct and crowded spiral lines.

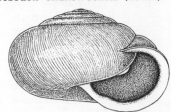

Figure 431. *Mesodon chilhoweensis* (Lewis)

92a Shell imperforate 93

92b Shell perforate or umbilicate..............................102

93a Shell diameter usually less than 15 mm.; usually very glossy. Fig.
   432..............................*Mesodon downieanus* (Bland)

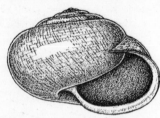

Figure 432. *Mesodon downieanus*
(Bland)

WIDTH: 10.5-14.7 mm. RANGE: Kentucky, Tennessee and Alabama.

Shell with 5-5½ whorls; pale yellow to greenish horn-colored; glossy; thin; sculptured with low, rounded rib-striae and crowded spiral lines. The shell is similar to *M. clausus* (see Fig. 442), but is smaller.

93b Shell larger, usually more than 15 mm. in diameter; usually only
   moderately glossy or dull...................................94
94a Shell marked with reddish-brown color bands. Fig. 433........
   ....*Triodopsis multilineata* (Say)

Figure 433. *Triodopsis multilineata*
(Say)

WIDTH: 14.5-32 mm. RANGE: Ohio to Mississippi, west to Minnesota, Nebraska and Arkansas.

Shell with 5½-6 whorls; ivory yellow to olive-buff, with dark reddish-brown bands; rather glossy. Sculptured with transverse striae and weak spiral lines.

94b Shell without color bands....................................95
95a Shell depressed 96
95b Shell globose to subglobose..................................98
96a Transverse striae low, fine; periphery of last whorl subangular.
   Fig. 434...............................*Mesodon roemeri* (Pfeiffer)

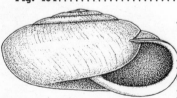

Figure 434. *Mesodon roemeri* (Pfeiffer)

WIDTH: 18-24 mm. RANGE: Texas.

Shell with 4½-5 whorls; cinnamon-buff to tan; usually narrowly umbilicate or perforate, but sometimes imperforate. Sometimes a parietal tooth is present, but it is often lacking.

172

96b Transverse striae raised and coarse; periphery of last whorl round **97**

97a Color of shell olive-brown; diameter usually greater than 20 mm. Fig. 435..........................*Mesodon indianorum* **(Pilsbry)**

WIDTH: 16-28.6 mm. RANGE: Arkansas and Oklahoma.

Shell with 4½-6 whorls; cream-buff to tannish-olive; somewhat glossy; sculptured with transverse striae and crowded, incised, spiral lines. The shell is similar to *Triodopsis divesta* (Fig. 436), but is more glossy and more finely striate.

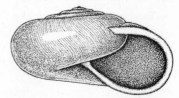

Figure 435. *Mesodon indianorum* (Pilsbry)

97b Color of shell cream to light brown; diameter usually less than 20 mm. Fig. 436..........................*Triodopsis divesta* **(Gould)**

WIDTH: 13.6-21 mm. RANGE: Missouri to Louisiana, west to Kansas and Oklahoma.

Shell with 4½-5 whorls; cream-colored; rather dull; depressed; imperforate. The shell of this species is similar to *Mesodon roemeri* (Fig. 434), but is smaller, with duller surface and coarser striae.

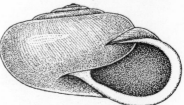

Figure 436. *Triodopsis divesta* (Gould)

98a Apertural margin of basal lip rounded. Fig. 437................ ....*Mesodon* **mitchellianus** **(Lea)**

WIDTH: 15.3-17.2 mm. RANGE: New York, west to Michigan and Kentucky.

Shell with about 5 whorls; pale yellowish-tan; sculptured with low, rounded rib-striae and wavy, impressed, spiral lines. The shell of this species differs from *M. clausus* (Fig. 442) by its closed umbilicus.

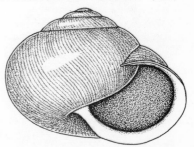

Figure 437. *Mesodon mitchellianus* (Lea)

98b Apertural margin of basal lip straight........................**99**

99a Reflected part of lip narrow. Fig. 438.......................
............................*Mesodon pennsylvanicus* (Green)

WIDTH: 15.2-20 mm. RANGE: Pennsylvania to Missouri.

Shell with 5½-6 whorls; light tan to pale yellowish-olive; sculptured with rather fine rib-striae and close, impressed, spiral lines. The whorls are rather closely coiled.

Figure 438. *Mesodon pennsylvanicus* (Green)

99b Reflected part of lip wide.................................**100**

100a Shell colored with an olive tint. Fig. 439......................
.................................*Mesodon andrewsae* Binney

WIDTH: 21.2-38.7 mm. RANGE: Virginia to Georgia, west to Tennessee and Alabama.

Shell with 5½-6 whorls; horn-colored to tannish-olive; sculptured with rather fine, low, rounded rib-striae, microscopic wrinkles, and close, wavy, spiral lines. Occasionally there is a tooth on the parietal wall.

Figure 439. *Mesodon andrewsae* Binney

100b Shell tannish or buff-colored..............................**101**

174

101a Shell spire relatively high. Fig. 440.... *Mesodon zaletus* **(Binney)**

WIDTH: 19-31 mm. RANGE: New York to North Carolina, west to Wisconsin, Iowa and Oklahoma.

Shell with 5½-6 whorls; cream-colored to cinnamon buff; sculptured with fine, oblique striae and microscopic spiral lines. The parietal wall usually has an oblique white tooth, but occasionally it is lacking.

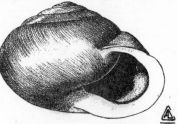

Figure 440. *Mesodon zaletus* (Binney)

101b Shell spire more depressed. Fig. 441.. *Triodopsis albolabris* **(Say)**

WIDTH: 17.6-45.3 mm. RANGE: Maine to Georgia, west to the Mississippi River; Oklahoma.

Shell with 5-6 whorls; cream-buff to pale tan; sculptured with rather fine, transverse striae and close, wavy, impressed, spiral lines. The shell is imperforate, its lip widely reflected.

Figure 441. *Triodopsis albolabris* (Say)

105a Spire high, shell rather globose. Fig. 442.. *Mesodon clausus* **(Say)**

Figure 442. *Mesodon clausus* (Say)

WIDTH: 12.5-19.5 mm. RANGE: Ohio to Georgia, west to Minnesota and Oklahoma.

Shell with 5-5½ whorls; pale yellow to light tan; rather glossy; sculptured with fine, close, transverse striae and microscopic spiral lines. The umbilicus is ½ covered to almost covered.

105b Spire more depressed, shell subglobose. Fig. 443..............
.... *Mesodon thyroidus* **(Say)**

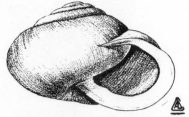

Figure 443. *Mesodon thyroidus* (Say)

WIDTH: 15-31 mm. RANGE: Massachusetts to Florida, west to Minnesota, Nebraska and Texas.

Shell with 5-5½ whorls; ivory-yellow to pale yellowish-green; somewhat glossy; thin; sculptured with fine transverse striae and minute spiral lines.

106a Upper part of apertural lip reflected. Fig. 444................
.... *Mesodon binneyanus* **(Pilsbry)**

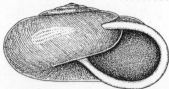

Figure 444. *Mesodon binneyanus* (Pilsbry)

WIDTH: 17.8-28.2 mm. RANGE: Arkansas and Oklahoma.

Shell with 4½-5½ whorls; light tannish-olive; glossy. The shell of this species is similar to *M. indianorum* (see Fig. 435), but the umbilicus is always partly open.

106b Upper part of apertural lip not reflected.....................107

107a Shell 16 mm. or less in diameter. Fig. 445....................
....................................*Mesodon kiowaensis* (Simpson)

WIDTH: 14-16 mm. RANGE: Arkansas and Oklahoma.

Shell with 5-5½ whorls; dark brown; sculptured with rather coarse transverse striae and fine, impressed spiral lines. A more robust form with larger aperture and smaller umbilicus has been named *M.k. arkansaensis* by Pilsbry.

Figure 445. *Mesodon kiowaensis* (Simpson)

107b Shell larger, 18 mm. or more in diameter. Fig. 446.............
.....................................*Mesodon roemeri* (Pfeiffer)

WIDTH: 18-24 mm. RANGE: Texas.

Shell with 4½-5 whorls; cinnamon-buff to tan; usually narrowly umbilicate or perforate, but sometimes imperforate. Sometimes a parietal tooth is present, but it is often lacking.

Figure 446. *Mesodon roemeri* (Pfeiffer)

108a Shell marked with reddish-brown color bands. Fig. 447.........
.....................................*Allogona profunda* (Say)

WIDTH: 19-34 mm. RANGE: New York to North Carolina, west to Minnesota, Iowa, Nebraska and Mississippi.

Shell with about 5½ whorls; light tan with a reddish-brown band above the periphery. The shell of this species differs from that of other large land snails in its area by the wide umbilicus (about 1/5 its diameter) and depressed spire.

Figure 447. *Allogona profunda* (Say)

108b Shell without color bands....................................109

109a Shell very large, 26 mm. or more in diameter. Fig. 448.........
...............................*Mesodon chilhoweensis* (Lewis)

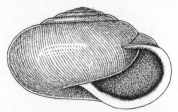

Figure 448. *Mesodon chilhoweensis* (Lewis)

WIDTH: 26.5-42 mm. RANGE: North Carolina and Tennessee.

Shell with 6-6½ whorls; cream-colored. The shell of this species differs from *M. sayanus* (see Fig. 430) by its size, its more broadly reflected lip, the absence of a basal tooth, and the more distinct and crowded spiral lines.

109b Shell smaller, 23 mm. or less in diameter....................110
110a Spire raised, shell subglobose. Fig. 449.......................
...........................*Mesodon sanus* (Clench and Archer)

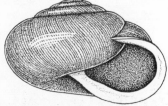

Figure 449. *Mesodon sanus* (Clench and Archer)

WIDTH: 17.5-20.6 mm. RANGE: Alabama.

Shell with 5-5½ whorls; yellowish-horn. The shell of this species is similar to that of *M. clausus* (see Fig. 442), but is more depressed, the umbilicus is wider, the whorls are more rounded and the lip is wider and more expanded.

110b Spire and shell very depressed. Fig. 450......................
...................................*Mesodon clenchi* (Rehder)

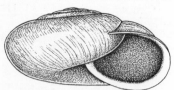

Figure 450. *Mesodon clenchi* (Rehder)

WIDTH: 19.8-22.2 mm. RANGE: Arkansas.

Shell with 4½-5 whorls; yellow; somewhat dull; rather thick; sculptured with fine, low, irregular transverse striae and irregular, impressed spiral lines. The lip is rather thick, its upper part not expanded.

111a First 1½ apical whorls smooth...........................112
111b First 1½ apical whorls sculptured with papillae or spiral striae.
...115

112a Shell less than 7 mm. in diameter. Fig. 451....................
.........................*Praticolella campi* Clapp and Ferriss

WIDTH: 5.8-6.2 mm. RANGE: Texas.

Shell with about 4 whorls; opaque white with translucent corneous bands; glossy; narrowly umbilicate. The shell of this species differs from the young of larger *Praticolella* species by its thickened and dilated lip.

Figure 451. *Praticolella campi* Clapp and Ferriss

112b Shell more than 7 mm. in diameter.......... 113
113a Aperture lip relatively thin; shell conspicuously banded. Fig. 452.
................................*Praticolella griseola* (Pfeiffer)

WIDTH: 8-13.7 mm. RANGE: Florida and Texas.

Shell with 4-5½ whorls; gray or white, with brown bands; somewhat glossy; narrowly umbilicate; sculptured with fine, irregular growth lines, nearly smooth. The shell is similar to *P. berlandieriana* (Fig. 454), but thinner.

Figure 452. *Praticolella griseola* (Pfeiffer)

113b Aperture lip relatively thick; shell with or without bands......114
114a Shell usually 9 mm. or less in diameter. Fig. 453..............
................................*Praticolella mobiliana* (Lea)

WIDTH: 7.3-9.1 mm. RANGE: Georgia, Florida and Alabama.

Shell with 5-6 whorls; pale cinnamon-buff. The shell of this species is similar to that of *P. jejuna* (Fig. 456), but has a deep furrow behind the lip, no spiral striae on the embryonic whorls and no whitish or cinnamon streak behind the lip.

Figure 453. *Praticolella mobiliana* (Lea)

114b Shell larger, more than 9 mm. in diameter. Fig. 454.............
.........................*Praticolella berlandieriana* (Moricand)

Figure 454. *Praticolella berlandieri-ana* (Moricand)

WIDTH: 9.3-14.5 mm. RANGE: Arkansas and Texas.

Shell with 4½-5½ whorls; white or gray to pale buff, typically with one or more olive-tan or brownish bands; solid; very narrowly umbilicate; sculptured with weak, irregular, transverse striae.

115a First 1½ apical whorls sculptured with papillae; shell usually 6 mm. or less in diameter. Fig. 455.......*Praticolella lawae* (Lewis)

Figure 455. *Praticolella lawae* (Lewis)

WIDTH: 5.7-6.1 mm. RANGE: North Carolina to Georgia, west to Tennessee and Mississippi.

Shell with 4½-5 whorls; pale cinnamon-buff; rather thin; very narrowly umbilicate; sculptured with indistinct growth wrinkles and very fine, short hairs or hair scars arranged in diagonal rows.

115b First 1½ apical whorls sculptured with spiral striae; shell larger, more than 6 mm. in diameter..............................116

116a Shell less than 9 mm. in diameter; body whorl without a furrow just preceeding the apertural lip. Fig. 456..*Praticolella jejuna* (Say)

Figure 456. *Praticolella jejuna* (Say)

WIDTH: 6.4-8.6 mm. RANGE: Georgia and Florida.

Shell with 4½-5 whorls; cinnamon-buff to pale olive-tan; sculptured with faint growth lines and close, uneven, microscopic wrinkling. There is a cinnamon or whitish streak behind the apertural lip.

116b Shell more than 10 mm. in diameter; body whorl with a furrow just preceeding the apertural lip. Fig. 457.................... ....*Praticolella bakeri* Vanatta

WIDTH: 10.5-11 mm. RANGE: Florida.

Shell with 5-5½ whorls; pale cinnamon-buff. The shell of this species is similar to *P. jejuna* (Fig. 456) and *P. mobiliana* (Fig. 453). It differs from *P. mobiliana* by the shallower furrow behind its apertural lip and the striate apical whorls.

Figure 457. *Praticolella bakeri* Vanatta

CAMAENIDAE

Although the Camaenidae are one of the most widespread land snail families in the world, they are represented in the eastern United States by only one introduced species, *Zachrysia provisoria*. The camaenids are medium to large helicid snails which lack a dart apparatus in the reproductive system.

Fig. 458.............................*Zachrysia provisoria* (Pfeiffer)

WIDTH: 25-29 mm. RANGE: Introduced into Florida from the western part of the Cuban mainland.

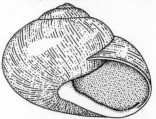

Shell with about 4½ whorls; yellow to horn-colored; somewhat glossy; rather solid; sculptured with rather even transverse striae. The aperture lip is not reflected, but is rather thick, particularly on the inside.

Figure 458. *Zachrysia provisoria* (Pfeiffer)

BRADYBAENIDAE

This family of snails with medium to small, depressed shells is native to eastern Asia. Only one species, *Bradybaena similaris*, has been introduced into the United States. Originally a native of the Chinese region, commerce had spread this species in tropical regions all around the world (Brazil, West Indies, Mauritius, Hawaii).

Fig. 459............................*Bradybaena similaris* (Férussac)

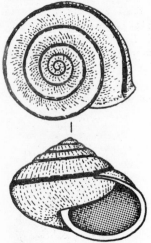

WIDTH: 12-16 mm. RANGE: Introduced into Louisiana.

Shell with about 5½ whorls; light brown, often with a single, spiral, chestnut band; sculptured with fine, irregular growth lines and fine spiral striae. The lip is reflected, its columellar portion partly covering the umbilicus.

Figure 459. *Bradybaena similaris* (Férussac)

HELMINTHOGLYPTIDAE

This family is native to North, Middle and South America. They are similar to the European Helicidae in that they have a dart apparatus in the reproductive system. Their shells are large to medium and vary in shape from conic to strongly depressed. The shells are umbilicate, perforate or imperforate, usually with expanded or reflected lips, and are often conspicuously marked with color bands. Only one species is found in the eastern United States.

Fig. 460....................................*Cepolis varians* (Menke)

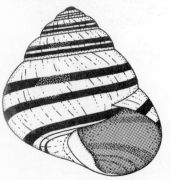

WIDTH: 14-16 mm. RANGE: Florida (and the Bahamas).

Shell with 3-6 whorls; white, usually with one or more spiral color bands; rather smooth, with low uneven transverse striae. The aperture is not reflected, but usually thickened along the inner margin.

Figure 460. *Cepolis varians* (Menke)

HELICELLIDAE

The Helicellidae are a large family of snails native to Europe, western Asia, and North Africa. Several species belonging to the genera *Cochlicella, Helicella* and *Hygromia,* have been introduced into the United States. They are all either umbilicate or perforate and of medium to small size. Their shapes are variable from long and rather narrow in *Cochlicella ventrosa* (Fig. 461), to broad and flat in *Hygromia striolata* (Fig. 464).

1a Shell wider than high..2

1b Shell higher than wide. Fig. 461....*Cochlicella ventrosa* (Férussac)

LENGTH: 9-12 mm. RANGE: Introduced into Florida and California from the Mediterranean countries.

Shell with 7-8 whorls; white, usually with reddish-brown transverse bands. The aperture is ovate-lunate, its outer lip sharp and not reflected. The columella is straight.

Figure 461. *Cochlicella ventrosa* (Férussac)

2a Shell with spiral color bands. Genus *Helicella*...................3

2b Shell without spiral color bands. Genus *Hygromia*..............4

3a Shell perphery rounded. Fig. 462.....*Helicella caperata* (Montagu)

WIDTH: 8-12 mm. RANGE: Introduced into Virginia from Western Europe (also introduced into southern Australia).

Shell with 5-6 whorls; white, with reddish-brown spiral bands; surface dull, opaque; umbilicate (umbilicus width about 1/5 that of the shell). The shell aperture is roundly-ovate, its outer lip not reflected, but often ringed inside with a calloused thickening.

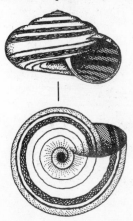

Figure 462. *Helicella caperata* (Montagu)

183

3b Shell periphery carinate. Fig. 463.......*Helicella elegans* (Gmelin)**

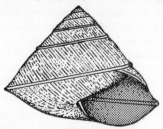

Figure 463. *Helicella elegans* (Gmelin)

WIDTH: 9-10 mm. RANGE: Introduced into South Carolina from the Mediterranean coasts of southern Europe and northwestern Africa.

Shell with about 6½ whorls; cream to light buff, with some olive-buff streaks and dots; glossy; umbilicate; sculptured with fine, but well-developed, transverse striae.

4a Periphery of last whorl obtusely angular. Fig. 464...............
.....................................*Hygromia striolata* (Pfeiffer)**

Figure 464. *Hygromia striolata* (Pfeiffer)

WIDTH: 10-11 mm. RANGE: Introduced into Canada and Massachusetts from Central Europe, France, and England.

Shell with 5-6 whorls; pale tawny-olive or brownish olive-buff, often with a pale band at the obtusely angular periphery. The young shells are covered with fine hairs, but these tend to be lost as the animal grows older.

4b Periphery of last whorl rounded. Fig. 465..*Hygromia hispida* (Linné)**

Figure 465. *Hygromia hispida* (Linné)

WIDTH: 7-9 mm. RANGE: Europe, central Asia to Siberia; introduced into Maine and Canada.

Shell with 5-6 whorls; pale cinnamon-brown. The shell of this species is very similar to that of *H. striolata* (Fig. 464), but is smaller, has rounded whorls, and the hirsute shell condition is often retained in adults.

HELICIDAE

The Helices comprise medium to large snails of European or west Asian origin and include the "edible snails" of Europe (*Helix pomatia, H. aspersa, Otala lactea* and *O. vermiculata*). The shell in this family is usually banded, generally wider than high and loosely coiled so that the central axial column is hollow or umbilicate. However, in the adult shell the umbilicus is often closed over by an expansion of the lip.

1a Aperture lip reflected. Genera *Cepaea, Helix* (in part) and *Otala*. .2

1b Aperutre lip not reflected, or only rarely slightly expanded. Genus *Helix* (in part). Fig. 466 . . . .*Helix pomatia* Linné

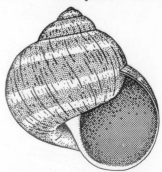

WIDTH: 32-45 mm. RANGE: Introduced into Michigan from Central Europe.

Shell with 4-5 whorls; light tan, with rather wide, uninterrupted, cinnamon-brown color bands; sculptured with fine spiral striae. The shell of this species is similar to *H. aspersa* (Fig. 471), but is usually larger, perforate to narrowly umbilicate (sometimes imperforate), has a duller surface, and has an unreflected, but sometimes slightly expanded, lip.

Figure 466. *Helix pomatia* Linné

2a Shell with fine spiral sculpture. Genus *Otala* 3

2b Shell without fine spiral sculpture 4

3a Shell sculptured with more or less continuous, fine, impressed spiral lines. Fig. 467 . . . .*Otala lactea* Müller

WIDTH: 27.5-36 mm. RANGE: Introduced into Georgia and Florida from Southern Spain and North Africa.

Shell with about 5 whorls; white, with reddish-brown spiral color bands flecked with white. The aperture and lip are dark brown. The shell is large, depressed, imperforate and spirally striate.

Figure 467. *Otala lactea* Müller

185

3b Shell sculptured with interrupted, fine, spiral wrinkles or malleations. Fig. 468.............................*Otala vermiculata* Müller

Figure 468. *Otala vermiculata* Müller

WIDTH: 28-34 mm. RANGE: Introduced into Louisiana from the Mediterranean countries.

Shell with about 5 whorls. This species is very similar to O. *lactea* (Fig. 467), but often has a higher spire, has a white aperture and lip, and is sculptured with spiral wrinkles or malleations instead of striae. Some individuals lack the spiral color bands.

4a Aperture lip white...5

4b Aperture lip reddish-brown to almost black. Fig. 469.............
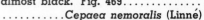
.....................................*Cepaea nemoralis* (Linné)

Figure 469. *Cepaea nemoralis* (Linné)

WIDTH: 22-24 mm. RANGE: Introduced into Ontario, Massachusetts, New York, New Jersey, Virginia, Tennessee, Pennsylvania, Wisconsin, Colorado (?) and California (?), from central and western Europe.

Shell with about 5 whorls; yellow, olive or red, usually with 1-5 reddish-brown bands. The whorls are rounded, the aperture ovate-lunate, the lip in adults reflected and colored dark brown to almost black.

5a Color bands continuous, but not always present. Fig. 470........
.....................................*Cepaea hortensis* (Müller)

Figure 470. *Cepaea hortensis* (Müller)

WIDTH: 16-21 mm. RANGE: Central and northern Europe; Iceland; Newfoundland; Maine, New Hampshire and Massachusetts.

Shell with about 5 whorls; yellow, usually with 1-5 reddish-brown bands. The shell of this species is very similar to that of C. *nemoralis* (Fig. 469), but it is smaller, is slightly higher spired, and it has a white instead of brown lip.

5b Color bands always present and interrupted by yellow flecks or streaks. Fig. 471 ....*Helix aspersa* Müller

WIDTH: 32-38 mm. RANGE: Introduced into South Carolina, Louisiana, Arizona and California. It is a native of Britain, western Europe, borders of the Mediterranean and Black Seas.

Shell with 4-5 whorls; yellow or horn-colored, with chestnut-brown spiral bands which are interrupted by yellow flecks or streaks. Shell large, globose, rather thin, imperforate or nearly so, moderately glossy, sculptured with fine wrinkles.

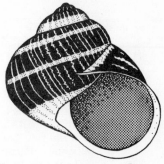

Figure 471. *Helix aspersa* Müller

SYSTEMATIC LIST OF EASTERN U.S. LAND SNAILS*

*This list is systematic down to the species, which are arranged alphabetically in their respective groups. The families occur in the text in the same order as they appear in this systematic list. Some of the taxonomic categories between *family* and *genus*, and between *genus* and *species* which occur in this list do not appear in the key. They are listed here for convenience. Such categories are often based entirely on characters of the internal anatomy, and such characters often do not parallel distinctive shell differences.

SYSTEMATIC LIST OF EASTERN U. S. LAND SNAILS

SYSTEMATIC LIST OF EASTERN U. S. LAND SNAILS

SYSTEMATIC LIST OF EASTERN U. S. LAND SNAILS

INDEX AND PICTURED-GLOSSARY

A

acerra, Ventridens 113, 195
Achatina 17
  fulica 17
Achatinidae 32, 122, 127, 196
acicula, Cecilioides 124, 197
ADNATE: closely attached; appressed.
aenea, Strobilops 65, 190
affinis, Strobilops 66, 191
Agricultural pests 17
Agriolimax 193
alabamensis, Vertigo 57, 59, 190
albilabris, Pupoides 47, 189
Albinula 50, 189
albolabris, Triodopsis 162, 175, 201
aldrichiana, Clappiella 86, 195
alliarius, Oxychilus 11, 93, 195
Allogona 11, 136, 177, 201
  profunda 177, 201
alternata, Anguispira 18, 75, 192
alternatus mariae, Bulimulus 134, 197
alticola, Columella 11, 48, 190
altispira, Stenotrema 143, 144, 146, 147, 198
American Indian 17
Amphibola 6
Amphineura 3, 4
andrewsae, Mesodon 174,199
andrewsae, Mesomphix 89, 194
andrewsae, Paravitrea 110, 194
Anguispira 8, 74, 192
  alternata 18, 75, 192
  clarki 75, 192
  cumberlandiana 74, 192
  kochi 11, 74, 192
ANGULAR: having an angle rather than a round contour. Fig. 472. 14

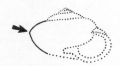

Figure 472

Angustula 56, 190
Annelid worms 4
anteridon, Triodopsis rugosa 167
Anus 4
aperta, Cecilioides 124, 197
APERTURE: the opening or "mouth" of a snail shell. Fig. 473. 1, 6, 16

Figure 473

APEX: the tip of a gastropod shell farthest away from its aperture. Fig. 474.

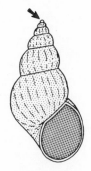

Figure 474

Aplacophorans 4
Appalachina 200
appressus, Mesodon 159, 161, 200
approxima, Retinella 97, 101, 193
arboreus, Zonitoides 11, 18, 107, 117, 196
Archeogastropoda 6, 23, 188
archeri, Mesodon 160, 200
Arion 8, 72, 192
  ater 11, 72, 74, 192
  fasciatus 11, 73, 192
  hortensis 11, 73, 192
  intermedius 11, 73, 192
  subfuscus 74, 192
Arionidae 28, 72, 192
arkansaensis, Mesodon kiowaensis 177
armifera, Gastrocopta 50, 189
Arthropods 3
arthuri, Vertigo 57, 63, 190
aspersa, Helix 11, 17, 185, 187, 202
asteriscus, Planogyra 44, 189
ater, Arion 11, 72, 74, 192

aulacogyra, Paravitrea 94, 108, 194
Aulacopoda 8, 27, 191
aurea, Pilsbryna 94, 98, 106, 107, 195
aurea, Succinea 191
auriculata, Polygyra 12, 151, 198
auriformis, Polygyra 151, 198
Austroriparian Province 10, 12
avara, Catinella 67, 191
avara, Polygyra 150, 198
AXIAL: parallel to the axis or columella of the shell; running across, or transverse to, the direction of the whorls; the opposite of "spiral."

B

bahamensis, Opisthosiphon 38, 188
bakeri, Praticolella 181, 199
Balance of life 17
barbatum, Stenotrema hirsutum 147
barbigerum, Stenotrema 138, 139, 199
BASAL: pertaining to, situated at, or forming, the base; pertaining to that part of the shell furthest from its apex; pertaining to the ventral part of the aperture lip.
BASAL TOOTH: calcareous deposit on the basal apertural lip. Fig. 475.

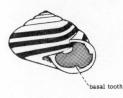

basal tooth

Figure 475

Basommatophora 6, 7, 24, 188
berlandieriana, Praticolella 179, 180, 199
bicolor, Gulella 120, 196
bilabiata, Truncatella 40, 188
binneyana, Retinella 11, 102, 193
binneyana, Vertigo 57, 60, 190
binneyanus, Mesodon 176, 200

BIRAMOSE: having two projecting parts or branches. Fig. 476.

Figure 476

BODY WHORL: the last whorl of a spiral gastropod shell, measured from the outer lip back to a point immediately above the outer lip. Fig. 477.

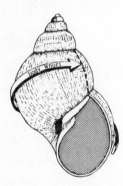

Figure 477

BREATHING PORE: opening in mantle or mantle edge for passage of air (or often water in aquatic species) into the air sac or lung cavity. Fig. 478. 16

C

CALCAREOUS: composed of carbonate of lime (calcium carbonate).

Calcium carbonate 1

CALLUS: a deposit of lime or shell material, often as a thickening near the umbilicus.

CAUDAL: situated in or near the tail or posterior end.
CAUDAL PIT: a conspicuous depression in the posterior dorsum of the foot of some snails which contains mucous glands. Fig. 479. 2

COLUMELLA: the internal column around which the whorls revolve; the axis of a spiral shell. Fig. 480. 15

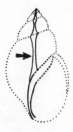

Figure 480

Columella 11, 48, 190
   alticola 11, 48, 190
   edentula 11, 48, 190
concavum, Haplotrema 120, 196
CONCENTRIC: about the same center, as in the case of lines of growth in some opercula. Fig. 481. 16

Figure 481

concordialis, Succinea 191
conecuhensis, Paravitrea 111, 117, 194
contracta, Gastrocopta 50, 189
CONTRACTILE: capable of reducing length by shortening and thickening. Fig. 482. 6, 7

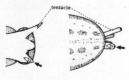

tentacle

Fig. 482

CORNEOUS: horn-like.
Cornu 202
corticaria, Gastrocopta 53, 189
costata, Vallonia 44, 45, 189
cragini, Triodopsis 164, 200

CRENULATE: scalloped or notched. Fig. 483. 14, 38

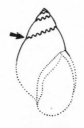

Figure 483

cristata, Gastrocopta 11, 51, 52, 189
cronkhitei, Discus 11, 76, 77, 192
cronkhitei catskillensis, Discus 77
Crop 1
cryptomphala, Retinella 100, 194
Cumberland Province 10, 12
cumberlandiana, Anguispira 74, 192
cumberlandiana, Retinella 97, 193
cupreus, Mesomphix 92, 194
cyclophorella, Vallonia 11, 45, 189

D

Daedalochila 148, 198
dalliana, Retinella 99, 102, 193
dealbatus, Bulimulus 11, 133, 197
decampi, Oxyloma 191
deceptum, Stenotrema 145, 198
decollata, Rumina 122, 123, 196
DECOLLATE: cut off, i.e. the top several whorls of the spire. Fig. 484. 38, 39

Figure 484

DECUSSATE: crossed.
Deflected 14
demissus, Ventridens 113, 114, 195
denotata, Triodopsis 158, 165, 201
dentatum, Chondropoma 38, 39, 188
dentifera, Triodopsis 162, 163, 201
depilatum, Stenotrema 144, 147, 198
DEPRESSED: flattened. Fig. 485. 14

Figure 485

Deroceras 8, 81, 82, 83, 193
   laeve 11, 83, 193
   reticulatum 11, 17, 82, 83, 193
DEXTRAL: wound or spiraled to the right when the shell is held so that the apex is up and the aperture facing the observer. Fig. 486. 14

Figure 486

Digestive tract 4, 8
dioscoricola, Pupisoma 49, 190
DISCOIDAL: round and flat like a disk. Fig. 487. 14

Figure 487

Discostrobilops 191
Discus 74, 75, 77, 192
   bryanti 76, 77, 192
   clappi 76, 77, 192
   cronkhitei 11, 76, 77, 192
   cronkhitei catskillensis 77
   macclintocki 76, 192
   patulus 76, 192
   rotundatus 75, 77, 192

Figure 488

Food 3, 16, 17, 18, 19

FOOT: the locomotory organ of mollusks; it is often variously modified for digging, grasping prey, etc. In snails it is the long, broad, ventral surface of the animal. Fig. 489. 1, 3, 4, 8

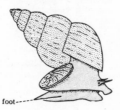

foot----

Figure 489

Figure 490

K

KEEL: a sharp edge; carina. Fig. 494.

Figure 494

Kidney 7, 8
kiowaensis, Mesodon 177, 200
kochi, Anguispira 11, 74, 192

L

labrosum, Stenotrema 139, 199
labyrinthica, Strobilops 66, 191
lactea, Otala 17, 185, 186, 202
Lacteoluna 135, 197
selenina 135, 197
laeve, Deroceras 11, 83, 193
LAMELLA: a fold, "tooth," or raised callus in the aperture of a shell.
Lamellaxis 8, 123, 125-127, 196
clavulinus 127, 196
gracilis 126, 127, 197
mauritianus 127, 197
micra 125, 197
Lamellibranchia 5
lamellidens, Paravitrea 106, 194
lasmodon, Ventridens 116, 195
lateumbilicatus, Zonitoides 118, 196
latior, Mesomphix 90, 194
latispira, Polygyra 155, 198
latissimus, Vitrinizonites 85, 194
lawae, Praticolella 168, 180, 199
lawae, Ventridens 113, 116, 195
leai, Stenotrema 140, 141, 169, 199
Lehmannia 11, 82, 193
poirieri 11, 82, 193
leporina, Polygyra 153, 154, 198
Leptodrymaeus 197
lewisiana, Retinella 99, 102, 193
ligera, Ventridens 113, 114, 195
Liguus 131, 197
fasciatus 131, 197
Limacidae 29, 81, 193
Limacinae 193

limatulus, Zonitoides 118, 196
Limax 11, 82, 193
flavus 11, 17, 82, 193
maximus 11, 17, 82, 193
Lime 12
Limnophila 7
LIMPET: a gastropod with a low, conical, unspiraled (or nearly so) shell. 4, 5
limpida, Vitrina 84, 196
LIP: edge of aperture of the shell; also called peristome. Fig. 495.

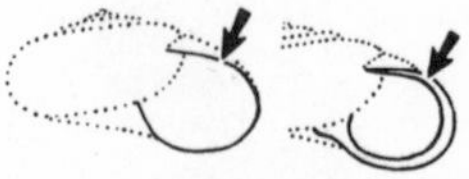

Figure 495

LIRAE: raised lines or ridges running in the same direction as the whorls. Fig. 496. 13

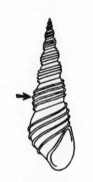

Figure 496

LIRATE: bearing raised spiral lines or ridges.
Liver Flukes 18
Lobosculum 198
LOOSELY COILED: having few, widely expanding whorls.
lubrica, Cionella 11, 18, 43, 189
Lucidella 6, 36, 188
tantilla 36, 188
LUNATE: shaped like a half-moon. 16
Lung 5
Lung cavity 8
Lung worms 18
luteola, Succinea 11, 191
Lyroconus 198

M

macclintocki, Discus 76, 192
macneilli, Pupisoma 49, 190
magazinensis, Mesodon 157, 200
magnifumosum, Stenotrema 143, 146, 147, 199
MALLEATE: dented as if hit by a hammer. 13
MANTLE: a membraneous flap or outer covering of the softer parts of a mollusk; it secretes the shell. Fig. 497. 1, 3, 4, 5, 7, 8, 16

Figure 497

MANTLE GROOVE: a longitudinal groove in the mantle of *Milax*. Fig. 498.

Figure 498

mariae, Bulimulus alternatus 134, 197
marmorea, Pallifera hemphilli 71
mauritianus, Lamellaxis 127, 197
maxillatum, Stenotrema 140, 199
Maxillifer 199
maximus, Limax 11, 17, 82, 193
Medical 17
Medical importance 17, 18
meridionalis, Striatura 11, 88, 196
Mesembrinus 197
Mesodon 11, 136, 147, 157, 159-164, 170-178, 199
andrewsae 174, 199
appressus 159, 161, 200
archeri 160, 200
binneyanus 176, 200
chilhoweensis 171, 178, 200
christyi 161, 169, 200
clarki 160, 200
clausus 172, 173, 176, 178, 199
clenchi 178, 200

Figure 499

Figure 500

N

O

Figure 501

OUTER LIP: the outer edge of the aperture. Fig. 502.

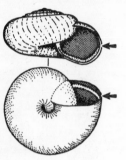

Figure 502

P

PALATAL: pertaining to the outer lip of a spiral gastropod shell. Fig. 503.

Figure 503

PALLIAL: pertaining to the mantle. 4, 7

PARIETAL: pertaining to the inner wall of the aperture; the part of the body whorl opposite the outer lip. Fig. 504.

Figure 504

PAUCISPIRAL: of few rapidly enlarging whorls or turns. Fig. 505. 15, 16

Figure 505

PEDAL GROOVE: a longitudinal groove in the body of a snail that marks the boundary where the tuberculate side wall of the foot joins the smooth ventral sole. Fig. 506. 8, 9

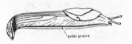

Figure 506

PENULTIMATE WHORL: the whorl before the last, or body whorl.
PERFORATE: having a minute opening at the base of the shell. Fig. 507. 15

Figure 507

PERIOSTRACUM: the chitinous external layer covering most mollusk shells.
PERIPHERY: the part of the whorl most distant from its central axis.
PERISTOME: edge of the aperture; also called "lip."

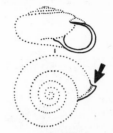

Figure 508

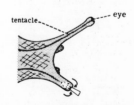

tentacle

eye

Figure 509

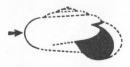

Figure 510

S

ing of mollusks. In some forms such as slugs, it is vestigial and contained inside the mantle, or lost entirely. 1, 3, 4, 5
SHOULDERED: Fig. 511. 14

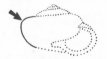

Figure 511

Figure 512

SLUG: a common designation for a snail without an external shell. The shell is either rudimentary and enclosed in the mantle or wanting entirely. Fig. 513. 1, 3, 4, 5, 8, 12, 16

Figure 513

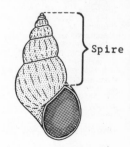

Spire

Figure 514

Figure 515

SUTURE: the line where one whorl of the shell is in contact with another. Fig. 516. 14

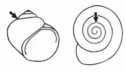

Figure 516

T

Figure 517

TOOTH: a short, usually high callus, or deposit of shelly material in the aperture of some shells; also a part of the radula.
Torsion 4
TRANSVERSE: at right angles to the direction of the whorls; parallel to the columella or axis of the shell.

Figure 518

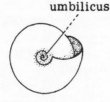